CHRISTMAS STORYBOOK

CHRISTMAS ☆ STORYBOOK

☆

By

OLIVE IRELAND THEEN

☆

☆

THE BRUCE PUBLISHING COMPANY
MILWAUKEE

✩

Nihil obstat:

    JOHN A. SCHULIEN, S.T.D.
    Censor librorum

Imprimatur:

    ✠ ALBERT G. MEYER
    Archiepiscopus Milwauchiensis

September 20, 1954

PN
6071
.C6
T48

To My Daughters
Karen and Virginia

CONTENTS

8   CONTENTS

CHRISTMAS STORYBOOK

THE FIRST CHRISTMAS*

MANY hundreds of years ago, a young girl named Mary lived in the little town of Nazareth. No one was so gentle, kind, and pure as Mary.

She often talked to God and asked Him to help her be good and holy. And God always heard her prayers, and planned for her the most wonderful thing that could happen to anyone. He planned that she would be the mother of His Son!

* Adapted from the New Testament.

God promised that one day He would send a Saviour into the world. When it was time, God called His angel Gabriel, and asked him to tell Mary.

In a glory of light the angel appeared to Mary and said, "Hail, full of grace, the Lord is with thee; blessed art thou among women!"

When Mary heard these words, she was troubled. But the angel, knowing her thoughts, said, "Fear not, for thou hast found grace with God. Behold, thou shalt bring forth a Son, and thou shalt call His name Jesus. He shall be great, and shall be called the Son of God, and of His kingdom there shall be no end!"

The angel's words made Mary very happy. She said, "Behold, the handmaid of the Lord, be it done to me according to thy word."

After the angel returned to heaven, Mary did not tell anyone about his visit. But the angel also told Mary that her cousin Elizabeth was to have a child. Mary was anxious to help her cousin who was old and would need someone.

So Mary went to see Elizabeth and Zachary. When Elizabeth saw Mary, she said, "Blessed is the fruit of thy womb." The Holy Ghost let Elizabeth know that Mary was to be the mother of the Saviour.

Mary stayed with Elizabeth three months. Then she returned to Nazareth, and to Joseph her husband.

One day soon after, Joseph noticed that Mary was

going to be a mother. He did not understand how this could be. But that night an angel came and told him not to be afraid to take Mary for his wife; that the Child was conceived by the Holy Ghost.

Having obeyed the angel, Mary and Joseph settled down to a quiet life. Joseph continued to do carpenter work, and Mary kept house for him.

Not long before Mary's Child was to be born, an order went out from the Roman Emperor that all his subjects should be enrolled in a census, and that each subject should register at the place of his birth. This meant that Joseph, of the house of David, had to go all the way to Bethlehem to be enrolled with Mary, his wife.

So Mary and Joseph started out on the journey. It was a long way to Bethlehem. The roads were often wet and slippery. Mary rode on a small donkey, while Joseph walked beside her.

They stopped to rest many times because Mary was weary and tired. But at last, after many days, they reached the little town of Bethlehem. It was crowded with visitors who had come to be enrolled in the census. The inns were filled. Everywhere that Joseph asked about a room, he was told, "We have no room here."

But one kind innkeeper told Joseph about a cave just outside the city that was used as a stable for animals in the winter. Perhaps they could use that. So Joseph and Mary went to the stable.

At midnight, in that cold poor stable, little Jesus, Son of God, was born! Mary wrapped the Holy Babe in swaddling clothes and laid Him in the manger.

Not far away some shepherds were taking care of their sheep. Suddenly an angel appeared to them, and the brightness of heaven shone about them. They were afraid, and hid their faces. The angel said to them, "Fear not, for I bring you good news of great joy which shall be to all people. For this day is born to you a Saviour, who is Christ the Lord, in the city of David. And this shall be a sign unto you: You will find the Infant wrapped in swaddling clothes and laid in a manger!"

Then the shepherds saw a great multitude of angels praising God and singing: "Glory to God in the highest, and on earth peace to men of good will."

And when the angels had returned to heaven, the shepherds said to one another, "Let us go over to Bethlehem and see this thing which has come to pass."

So they left their flocks and hastened to the town of Bethlehem where they found Mary and Joseph, and the Holy Babe lying in a manger. They knelt and worshiped the newborn King. Then they presented Him the gifts they had brought.

And seeing the Infant sleeping peacefully, they returned to their flocks, glorifying and praising God for all they had seen and heard.

They made known to many the heavenly miracle at

Bethlehem. And everyone thanked God and praised Him for sending the Saviour.

When Baby Jesus was forty days old, Mary and Joseph prepared to take Him to the Temple. Every mother, according to the Law, brought her first baby boy to the Temple to be presented to the Lord.

So Joseph and Mary, with little Jesus, started on their journey to the Temple.

As they drew near, they stopped and bought two white doves. This was to be their offering to God. The law said that the parents of the child to be presented should make a sacrifice to God.

At the Temple was an old man named Simeon, who had come to the Temple to pray. He was a good and holy man who often talked with God. One day God said, "Some day, Simeon, you shall see Jesus."

When Simeon saw Mary and Joseph bringing the Child Jesus, he went up to them and took the Baby in his arms. Simeon was very happy, for he knew he was holding the Son of God. He lifted his eyes to heaven and thanked God for letting him see the Promised One before he died. Lovingly, he held the Infant Jesus, and told Mary that many people would not like her Son and would not accept His teachings. He told her that she, too, would suffer much. "A sword of sorrow shall pierce thy heart," he said to her.

It happened, on that day, that an old woman named

Anna was waiting at the Temple to see Jesus. She spent her time praying and fasting. When she saw Jesus, she was very happy and praised God for His goodness to her. She told everyone that she had seen the Saviour in the Temple with his parents.

Mary and Joseph left the Temple, and returned to their home. They marveled at the things that were said about Jesus.

Now, in the far-off country of Arabia, lived three Wise Men named Melchior, Balthazar, and Casper. They were called the Magi, for they were the wisest of men. They studied the secrets of the skies and stars, of planets and herbs, and ancient writings.

Among the ancient writings they studied was one by the wise old prophet Balaam, who said, "In the latter days, there shall come a star out of Jacob, and a scepter shall spring up from Israel."

The Wise Men knew this meant that one day a bright new star would come into the sky. It would be the sign of the coming of the new King who would govern and rule the people of Israel.

One night, while the Wise Men were watching from the balcony of their home, a bright new star stood over the western mountains. The Wise Men knew this was the sign they had been waiting for. They were eager to follow the star, and quickly made ready for the journey.

When they left their home in the east, they were

richly dressed in velvet robes and jeweled rings. And in beautiful carved boxes they carried myrrh, frankincense, and gold for the new King.

They followed the star to Jerusalem. At the palace of King Herod they asked, "Where is He that is born King of the Jews? For we have seen His star in the east, and have come to worship Him."

Herod was troubled at what the Wise Men said. He did not want a new King to take his place. So he dismissed the Wise Men, and called the Chief Priests and Scribes, and asked them where the Christ Child would be born.

They said, "In Bethlehem of Judea, for so it is written by the prophet, that out of Bethlehem shall come the Captain that shall rule over Israel."

When Herod heard these words, he was very angry. He sent the Scribes and Priests away and called the Magi to him secretly. But he hid his anger, and said, "Go and search for the Child, and when you have found Him, bring me word again, that I also may come and worship Him."

So the Wise Men rode out from Herod's palace. And the star which they saw in the east, went before them until it stood over where the young Child was.

The Wise Men found the house and went in. They saw the Holy Child with Mary, His mother. And kneeling down, they worshiped Him. Then they presented Him the treasures they brought, myrrh, frankincense, and gold. And having been warned in a dream not to tell Herod where the Christ Child was, they returned to their own home secretly, by another way.

When the Wise Men had gone, an angel of the Lord appeared to Joseph in his sleep and said, "Arise, and take the Child and His mother and flee into Egypt; and be there until I tell you. For it will come to pass that Herod will seek the Child to destroy Him."

Quickly, Joseph arose and told Mary about the angel's warning. They agreed to hurry away. They took only a few belongings for they wanted to travel light. Mary wrapped the sleeping Jesus in a blanket and went off into the lonely night with Joseph to Egypt.

Herod waited in vain for the Wise Men to return to him. And when he knew they had tricked him, he became very angry. He ordered his soldiers to kill every little boy baby in and around Bethlehem that was two years old or younger. In this way he hoped to destroy the newborn King.

But Jesus was not killed. Joseph and Mary were far away in the desert on their journey into Egypt.

Jesus, Mary, and Joseph lived in Egypt until Herod died. Then an angel appeared to Joseph, saying, "Arise, and take the Child Jesus and His mother, and go back into the land of Israel. For he is dead who sought the Child's life."

This was good news for Mary and Joseph. They had wanted many times to go back to their home in Israel. And with hope in their hearts, they left Egypt. Nearing home, they heard that Herod's son was now ruling in Jerusalem. Herod's son was cruel like his father, so Joseph and Mary decided to settle in the town of Nazareth instead.

☆
☆

MARY AND JOSEPH

☆

☆

MARY's father was a shepherd. He had come from a family of kings, but now he was very poor. His name was Joachim and his wife's name was Anne.

When Mary was born, her parents were very old. They had prayed to God many years to bring them a child. When God sent them Mary, they were very pleased.

There was not another little girl in Nazareth who was so good and kind to everyone. Wherever Mary went, people would say, "Isn't she the loveliest little girl!"

Mary liked to pray, and often went to the synagogue with her parents. She liked to talk to God and feel His nearness. She asked God to help her be a good girl.

Mary's soul was always pure and holy. She was born with a pure soul. From the time of her very beginning before she was born, God meant that she should be full of grace. God wanted her to be the mother of His Son, Jesus.

When Mary was a young girl, she promised herself to God's service. But because it was God's will, she agreed to be married to a man named Joseph, of the house of David.

One day, after Joseph had returned from the Feast of the Passover in Jerusalem, he went to see Mary's parents. He wanted to tell Joachim about the happenings of the great feast. He knew that Joachim longed to go, but was too old to make the journey.

As he was preparing for the visit, he thought about the young girl Mary whom he would meet soon. Ever since she had moved to town, he had wanted to know her. He had seen her many times, in the synagogue, carrying water from the well, or taking care of her parents. She was quiet and shy; he knew she was a good girl. The way she walked and talked showed how truly fine she was. When he had seen her among the anemones and lilies, he had wanted to go over to her and talk with her.

Joseph had never thought of getting married before.

Now he did think of it, and he wanted only Mary for his wife.

When he was finished making himself attractive for Mary, he left his home and walked to her house. The closer he got, the more he thought about her. "This night," he said, "I will ask her parents if I may marry her."

And when he entered her home, Anne, Joachim, and Mary were just finished with their evening meal.

"Joseph," said Joachim, "come in and meet my wife Anne, and my daughter Mary. And come sit down with us at the table."

"Thank you, but I have already eaten," said Joseph.

"Then we will go into the other room and you can tell Anne and me about the Passover," said Joachim. "I know you were there, for Samuel told me."

But Joseph's mind was not on the Passover, and he was eager to change the subject. All he could think of was the lovely young girl Mary, who was busy clearing away the supper dishes from the table.

"Good father Joachim, and mother Anne," said Joseph eagerly, "I have come to ask permission to marry your daughter. I love her and want her for my wife."

Joseph told them he had saved his money for some time, and that he would take good care of their daughter. "I have been very lonely since my parents died," he said.

"You are a good man, Joseph," said Joachim. "I knew

your father Jacob and your mother. They were my friends. From all the men in Galilee, I would choose you as the husband of my daughter. I give you my blessing and hope you will have the blessings of the Lord."

But Anne sat silent. She felt sad to think that Mary would be leaving her home. But she knew that Joseph would be a good husband. "I give you my blessing, too, Joseph," she said.

Joseph was pleased that he had been accepted and was eager to tell Mary.

Now Mary was in the other room, but she heard what Joseph had said about her. She was happy that he wanted her to be his wife. She had noticed Joseph about the village and knew he was a good man. Many times she had seen him at the synagogue.

When Mary came back into the room, her mother said, "Mary, my daughter, Joseph wants you for his wife."

Mary smiled at Joseph, and took his hand. Joseph looked deep into her lovely blue eyes and said, "I have been talking to your parents, Mary, and have told them I want you for my wife. Will you marry me?"

"I will be glad to be your wife, Joseph," she said. "I am happy that you asked me. You are a good dependable man. Soon I will be sixteen. We can be married on my birthday, if it is all right with you."

The thought of his marriage to Mary filled Joseph with happiness. He knew he was a lucky man.

On her sixteenth birthday, Mary was married to Joseph. They were very happy, and lived in a little limestone house just inside the gates of the city. Joseph worked as a carpenter, and Mary kept house for him.

One day, while Mary was kneeling in prayer, a wonderful thing happened to her. God sent the angel Gabriel to visit her! God wanted Mary to be the mother of His Son. He knew she was free from sin, and that her soul always had the gift of sanctifying grace which makes it holy and pleasing to God.

From a great light, the angel appeared to her. For a moment Mary was dazzled by the bright light around her. The angel smiled at her and his eyes seemed to bless her. He was dressed in a white garment and from the light he said, "Hail, full of grace! The Lord is with thee; blessed art thou among women!"

Mary was afraid and troubled. She wondered why God should send an angel to her. The angel, knowing her thoughts, said, "Fear not, Mary, for you have found grace with God. You shall have a Son and you should call His name Jesus. He shall be great and shall be called the Son of the Most High. The Holy Ghost shall come upon you and your Child shall be called the Son of God. Behold, your cousin Elizabeth shall also have a son in her old age, for nothing is impossible with God."

Mary believed all that the angel said to her. She knew that God had sent him. She was willing to do what God asked of her, so she said, "Behold the handmaid of the Lord; be it done to me according to thy word."

Mary was happy that she was to be the mother of the Saviour of the world. For a long time after the angel had disappeared, she thought of the wonderful thing that had happened to her.

The angel had said that her cousin Elizabeth would have a son in her old age. This news made Mary very happy. She knew that Elizabeth was all alone. She made up her mind to go to her and help her. But first she must speak to Joseph.

She knocked softly at the door of his carpenter shop. Joseph opened the door and was delighted to see her standing there.

"Good morning, Mary," he said. "What can I do for you this morning?"

And then Mary told Joseph that she wished to visit her cousin Elizabeth.

Joseph did not like to have Mary go so far away. But he knew she wanted to go. He said, "I hate to have you leave me, but since you wish, I shall help in making the arrangements for the journey."

So Mary went to see Elizabeth and her husband Zachary. It was a long and tiresome journey over the valleys and hills, but Mary did not mind. She was only thinking of how much her cousin needed her.

At last, tired from the long journey, Mary came to

the house of her cousin in Ain Karim. Elizabeth was surprised, but very happy to see her. In her heart she heard the voice of the Holy Ghost telling her that Mary was to be the mother of the Son of God. She threw her arms around Mary and said, "Blessed is the fruit of thy womb! Who am I that the Mother of my Lord should come to me?"

"My soul praises God for all the wonderful things He has done for me," Mary said. "I am lowly and poor, but He has made me great. Behold, from this time on, all people shall call me blessed!"

Mary stayed with Elizabeth three months. She helped care for the baby John. Then she returned to Nazareth.

When she saw Joseph, all was well again with her. She was happy to be back in her own little home, cooking and caring for Joseph, and awaiting the birth of her Son.

THE JOURNEY TO BETHLEHEM

I⊤ WAS almost dark when Joseph returned to his home one night from the market place. He had attended a meeting to discuss the decree that had come from Caesar Augustus. He knew he could not work any longer in his carpenter shop, so he put away his tools for the night. Before going to the room where Mary was, he had to care for his donkey.

Now Mary and Joseph had a small house. One room

was for living purposes, the other for Joseph's carpenter shop. It was into this shop that Joseph led his donkey. He used the shop as a stable at night, because he could not afford to build a separate one. He did not want to let the donkey out at night, for he might run away or be stolen. The donkey was useful to him in his work. He hauled heavy logs and loads of straw.

Joseph made up the donkey's bed with the straw he had piled in the corner of the shop. He fed the animal, and locked the door securely for the night.

In the meantime, Mary had made a fresh fire and had lighted the candle so that the room would be warm and bright when Joseph came in from the cold. When he entered, Mary was busy making his supper.

"Mary," said Joseph, "how do you feel this evening?"

"I am very well tonight, Joseph," she answered, fixing the fish they were having for supper. "Come kneel beside me, and we will say our prayers. Then we will eat, for I know you must be hungry."

And after supper, Joseph told Mary that a decree had come from Caesar Augustus that all his subjects should be enrolled in a census. And that each subject was to go to the place of his birth to register.

"I don't like to leave you, Mary," Joseph said, "but I must obey the king's order and go to Bethlehem. There is no need for you to go because I can enroll your name with my own. You and I are both of the house of David."

"Unless I am delayed," he continued to say, "I can walk to Bethlehem in three or four days. It will take me one day to enroll and get ready for the return trip. I should be back in Nazareth in about ten days. I hope you will not be afraid to stay alone. Perhaps you could find someone to stay with you while I am away."

Mary listened to the words of her husband, and in her heart she thanked God for such a good and thoughtful man. She knew that Joseph always thought of her comfort before his own. She knew he was thinking that it would be too hard a journey for her to make since she was to have a baby soon.

Mary thought and thought about Joseph and the trip. Since he had to go, she would go with him. She would stand all the hardships of the journey, for she did not want to be separated from her husband for so long a time.

"Joseph," Mary said, "I will go with you to Bethlehem. It will be all right. Do not worry about me. I know that God will take good care of me on the journey."

Joseph was glad that Mary would go with him. He said, "It is as God wants it. I will take good care of you on the journey. It is settled then; we will go together."

Mary and Joseph awoke early the next day. There was much to be done in preparation for the journey.

After they had said their morning prayers, they ate their breakfast of bread, fish, and water. For a while, Mary was busy wrapping clothing and food for the journey. Most of the clothes she wrapped were for the baby who would be born soon. She baked bread, filled a bottle with wine, another with oil, and still another with fresh water.

Joseph put away his tools and closed up the carpenter shop. The donkey, made ready for the trip, stood outside the house.

When all was ready, Mary and Joseph knelt down and prayed that God would bless them, and that they would have a safe journey. Then they put on their cloaks. Mary threw her heavy wool shawl over her arm and went outside. Joseph took up his staff, threw their bundle of food and clothing over his shoulder, and followed Mary outside. He put Mary upon the donkey, and led the little animal down the hill. Mary felt a little sad to be leaving her lovely house.

Soon they had passed the well just outside the walls of the city, and Nazareth was behind them. They passed through the groves of olive trees and headed into the plains of Esdraelon. Here and there they could see men busy plowing and planting their fields.

By noon, they had traveled about seven miles, and were nearing the town of Jezreel. They stopped just outside the walls of the city and rested at one of the many springs. Before going on, they refilled their water bottle.

Ahead of them were the mountains of Samaria. It would be rough going through the mountains. When they reached the foot of the mountains, they lay down and slept.

The next morning found them going through the worst part of their journey. Mary walked now and then beside Joseph because she wanted to spare the little donkey. The paths were rough and slippery from the new fallen snow. On and on they plodded, ever so slowly, because Mary was tired and feeling the effects of the trip. They made camp for the night in the mountains. Joseph knew it was yet a long way to Engannin, and he did not want to hurry Mary. She was looking pale, and shivering from the cold. Joseph spread their blankets on the ground and they ate and went to sleep.

In the morning, they continued on the journey through the mountains. By noon, they had traveled many miles. But Joseph stopped and made a fire to warm Mary. It was cold and there was a fine misty rain falling. With some warm wine and dry clothes, Mary felt able to continue.

"Tonight," said Joseph, "I will find a room at an inn for you. You should not have slept on the ground last night. It was not good for you."

And just before dark, they reached the inn at Engannin. Joseph helped Mary off the tired little donkey, and they went in. Joseph made Mary comfortable for the night. "You are so good to me, Joseph," she said. "I could not have gone this far without your help."

Before sunrise Mary and Joseph had left the inn and were traveling toward the city of Sebaste in the mountains ahead. And at noon, they could see the city, high up on the top of the mountain. They did not stop, but went on until they reached the outskirts of the city of Sichem, a few miles away.

"This is the valley where Abraham built an altar to God," Mary said. "It is a lovely place with its gardens and orchards of good fruit trees. I would like to stay here for the night, Joseph."

"Then we will stay, Mary," said Joseph. And they slept that night among the flowers and fruit trees.

The sun was bright and warm when they awoke the next morning. Mary and Joseph were rested and eager to continue. After saying their morning prayers, they ate and left.

Going over the rocky mountain slopes was hard for Mary. She walked beside Joseph, leaning on him many times. It grew colder toward the middle of the day and a rainstorm came up. The wind was cold, and Mary wrapped her shawl more closely about her. Joseph was kind and let Mary rest many times as they went through the mountains.

"Soon we will be in Jerusalem," said Joseph, trying hard to be cheerful for Mary's sake. In the distance was the hill country of Judea, and they were glad, for this was friendly territory. Before nightfall, they had passed the city of Beeroth. Joseph was eager to get to Bethlehem, and they pushed on steadily.

But it began to rain hard, and Joseph sought shelter for Mary. It was almost dark when they entered a small village. Joseph took Mary to an inn, and they dried their wet garments by a fire.

But it was several days before they neared Jerusalem. Mary was very tired. The little donkey could only go so fast now; he, too, was exhausted from the long journey. The closer they got to Jerusalem, the more anxious Joseph became, for Mary said that her time was near at hand. But still they did not hurry. At noon, they stopped again to eat and rest near an open spring.

On one late afternoon of the journey it grew cold. The wind was strong and the rain turned into snowflakes that whirled about them. It was still daylight when they reached Jerusalem. On a hilltop near the city, Mary and Joseph rested and prayed that they would make it to Bethlehem by nightfall.

They did not stay long at Jerusalem, but went steadily on toward Bethlehem just a few miles away. Joseph wanted to get to Bethlehem so that Mary could be made comfortable. But Mary, seated on the donkey, felt warm inside, though she shivered from the cold. She knew that her Son would be born soon in the town just ahead. Joseph led the donkey down the rocky hillside, and watched closely that Mary did not fall.

"Mary, just ahead is Bethlehem!" Joseph said, with hope in his heart. "We will find an inn and you may rest again."

When they could see Bethlehem, Mary's thoughts were more and more about the birth of her Son.

They were nearing the town now, passing fields and orchards. They saw many shepherds keeping watch over their goats and sheep. It was dark when they came to an inn. Joseph inquired if they might have a room.

"Kind sir," said Joseph to the innkeeper, "could my wife and I have a room? My wife is not well; we need shelter for the night."

The innkeeper looked at Mary. She looked tired. "I cannot feel sorry for her," he thought. "There are others to be considered.

"The inn is filled with visitors who have come to be enrolled in the census," he said to Joseph. "If you had only come a little earlier, I could have given you a room. But there is a stable near the town that is used for animals in the winter. You may have that."

Joseph was so disappointed, he could hardly speak. But Mary, understanding, said, "Come, Joseph, we will go to the stable. We can be by ourselves, and it will not be too cold."

And it was in that lowly stable near Bethlehem, at midnight, that Mary's divine Son, Jesus, was born.

ON THE HOLY NIGHT*

☆

☆

ON THE Night of Nights, just an hour before the Christ
Child was born, a strange silence fell upon Bethlehem.
"The wind was stilled, birds stopped singing, bare trees
put forth green leaves, rivers stopped in their flow, flowers
bloomed upon the icy ground; the animals knelt in
adoration of the Infant King. . . ."

The first to break the strange silence were the angels,
telling the shepherds on the hillside near Bethlehem that

* Adapted, in part, from "The Welcome of Nature," *Catholic Digest,*
December, 1937; no author given.

the Christ Child was born. When the angels sang "Glory to God in the highest" all nature joined in the song of praise. And the wind carried the sweet music of the angels' song far and wide.

On the first Christmas night the animals were given the power of speech so they could praise God and tell everyone about the birth of Jesus.

The first animal to speak was the cock, who flapped his wings and chanted "Christ is born." And the crow heard the cock, and wanted to know what time it took place. So he cawed, "When, when?"

In the forest, the mighty lion heard the news of Christ's birth, and roared with all his might, "Today Christ is born."

The cow wanted to know where the Christ Child was born, so she lowed, "Where, where?"

The sheep heard the angels telling the shepherds the "good news of great joy" and bleated the answer, "He is born in Bethlehem."

And the donkey wanted all to visit the stable at Bethlehem and see the Holy Child, so he brayed, "Let us go to Bethlehem."

A little lark rose high in the air, as if to lead the way, and trilled, "To adore Him."

The dogs barked, "We should go to Bethlehem," and the horse whinnied, "Hee . . . He is born in Bethlehem."

All the animals offered their services to the Holy Infant

and the Blessed Mother Mary. The lowliest of all God's creatures, the worm, was the first in the stable to offer service to the Holy Child.

It was so dark in the stable that Mary could not see to put on the little garments of the Baby Jesus. A little worm, seeing how hard it was for her, crept along the floor to a slit in the door through which the moonlight was shining. He took a ray of light and carried it along until he reached the Blessed Mother. Then he climbed up her cloak and settled on her knee so that she could see by the light.

The little Saviour was so pleased, he said to the little worm, "Dear little worm, your kindness to My mother shall be rewarded. I make you a present of the light. You shall never lose it."

Then the little worm was placed on the edge of the manger bed where it took the place of a night light. And ever since, it has been known as the glowworm.

In the stable, the ox and the ass adored the Holy Infant. They, too, helped the Blessed Mother and Jesus. The ox stood up and breathed upon the Baby to keep Him warm. And she was very careful that her great horns did not hurt Jesus in any way. When she moved about in the stable, she was very careful not to step on Jesus or frighten Him. And sometimes, if Jesus was awake, she would move her great ears back and forth to entertain Him.

And the ass leaned against a crack in the stable wall to protect the Infant from the cold draft. He was quiet and moved about noiselessly so as not to awaken the sleeping Babe. He was always careful not to bray in the Infant's face; and when he heard strange noises that sounded like danger, he would raise his ears high to show Mary and Joseph that strangers might be near. And sometimes he stood at the entrance of the stable so that wild animals could not come in and harm Jesus. But of all the services he offered, the one he liked best was carrying the Blessed Mother and Jesus on their flight into Egypt.

It was God's animals, which were not dumb, that brought gifts and offered services to the Blessed Mother and the Infant Jesus on that holy night, the first Christmas.

THE CHRISTMAS STAR*

Long, long ago, God created the stars in the heavens. But He looked upon one certain star with special love. It was to be the most beautiful star of all. For it was God's plan that the light of this star would announce an important event.

The story begins in the country of Arabia with the

* Adapted, in part, from "God Created a Special Star," by Rev. Father Kiernan, in the *Catholic Register*, December, 1948.

three men who were students of the sky. They were the
Wise Men. Their names were Melchior, Balthazar, and
Casper. In their long years of studying the stars, they
had looked forward to seeing a certain star whose light
was soon to reach the earth. For in the Scriptures of the
Jews, whose God they worshiped, they found the reason
for its coming: "A star shall rise out of Jacob and a scepter
shall spring up from Israel."

It was in the spring of the year that the three Wise
Men met again as they had done so many times before.
At the palace of the eldest of the kings, Melchior, they
met to discuss their favorite topic, the mysterious star.
For days they studied their charts and scrolls to deter-
mine the date of the star's appearance. When they finished
their work, there seemed to be a gleam of hope in their
eyes. Perhaps their dreams would soon come true.

The sun was sinking in the west as Casper and Balthazar
prepared to leave Melchior's home. And when they were
ready to leave, Melchior said, "As we part again, my
brothers, I feel our hopes may soon be fulfilled. Be watch-
ful in these nights to come. When the Star of Peace
appears, set forth at once. We will meet at the place
in the oasis agreed upon. Wait there for one another.
God willing, we will set forth on the third day." And so
he bade them farewell.

One December midnight of that same year the special
star shone on earth. When it appeared, the three faithful

men were hopefully watching the skies. Its beauty was far greater than they had expected!

Though the three Wise Men lived many miles apart, their hearts and souls were joined at that moment. Their joy was very great. In the stillness of that wonderful night, their hearts cried out, "The long awaited King has come!" They knelt in silent prayer of thanksgiving. And as they watched the star, they thought they heard angelic music singing, "Glory to God in the highest, and on earth peace to men of good will."

Without delay, each King set out from his own city to the place in the desert where they were to meet. Casper was the first to arrive. It was past midnight and he grew worried when he could not see the others coming. But on the morning of the first day, just at sunrise, Casper's heart beat fast with joy as he saw two caravans on the far horizon. These travelers were his faithful friends. "Thank God!" Casper said. "Now we can go together in search of the Holy One."

Later the caravans passed through the gates of Jerusalem on the way to Herod's palace. There they said to Herod, "Where is He that is born King of the Jews? For we have seen His star in the east and have come to worship Him."

King Herod was troubled. He sent for his Chief Priests and Scribes and asked them where the Christ should be born. And they said, "In Bethlehem of Judea, for it is written by the prophet: 'And thou, Bethlehem, in the land of Juda, art not the least among the princes of Juda; for from thee shall come forth the Captain that shall rule My people Israel.' "

Then Herod called the Wise Men to him and said, "Go and search for the Child, and when you have found Him, bring me word again, that I also may come and adore Him." And the Wise Men went away.

"And behold, the star which they saw in the east, went before them until it came and stood over where the Child Jesus was. And seeing the star, they rejoiced with exceeding great joy. And entering into the house, they found the Child with Mary, His mother, and falling down they adored Him, and opening their treasures, they offered Him gifts: gold, frankincense, and myrrh. And having received an answer in sleep that they should not return to Herod, they went back another way into their own country."

Once more the Wise Men stopped at the oasis where they had met. And around their campfire they talked about the miracle they had seen. Casper, the youngest, was much troubled, and said, "Good father Melchior, I fear for this Child. Who will call Him king? He lives in such a poor and humble place!"

And the wise old Melchior said, "I too felt the same way when I saw how poor the little Saviour was. But when I looked at His Blessed Mother, her eyes seemed to speak to me and say, 'Good sir, be not troubled at what you see, but adore your King. And know ye that my Son will one day proclaim: I am a King; for this I was born, For this I have come; But My kingdom is not of this world.' "

☆
☆

STAR FLOWERS OF BETHLEHEM

☆

☆

ON THE Holy Night, the blazing Star of Bethlehem shone
so bright that all the other stars were blotted out. But
still the midnight sky was so full of sparkling rays and
splendid colors, that the night was turned almost into day.

A few miles from Bethlehem, a shepherd girl named
Ruth lay on her straw bed in the corner of the small
hut where she lived with her father and mother. Her
mother had gone to bed hours ago. Her father was out

tending the sheep. During the day, Ruth used to watch the goats and sheep for her father, so that he could rest and sleep.

But for many days and nights Ruth had lain in her bed, too sick to be up and about. She was still too weak to help her tired father tend the sheep. He wanted her to get well, and promised he would take her with him to Bethlehem when he sold his sheep and goats.

From her small window Ruth could see the stars twinkling in the skies. Often she made up pictures of animals and other figures from the formations of the stars. But her favorite pastime was reciting the little verse she had made up about the stars:

> High in the heavens
>   You twinkle all night;
> A precious jewel
>   That sparkles so bright.
>
> You're God's own secret,
>   Whatever you are;
> So twinkle brightly
>   God's little star.

In the middle of the night, Ruth noticed that her room became very bright. She raised herself up and looked out of the window. In the distance, she could see a bright star shimmering in the heavens. "Why is the star so bright," she thought, "and what can this mean?" And then, weak and trembling, she got up and knelt at the window. The brightness seemed to be over where her father was watching over the sheep. Could she be dreaming all this?

"Mother," Ruth called, "wake up, and see the light and the bright star!" But her mother was still tired and sleepy, so she said, "Child, get back into your bed. You will not get well if you get up so soon."

"But mother," said Ruth, "the midnight sky is full of light! Come to the window and see what it is."

"You are dreaming, my child," her mother said.

And then Ruth heard the most beautiful song in all the world. It sounded like the angels were singing, "Glory to God in the highest." From her window she saw a host of angels in the sky.

"It must be a miracle," she thought. Then she remembered all the things her parents had told her about the coming of the Christ Child.

Ruth watched until the light faded and the earth was dark again. Then she lay down on her bed and fell asleep.

In the morning, her mother came in to see her. "Ruth, you are looking much better this morning. There seems to be some color in your cheeks. Did you sleep well last night?"

Ruth did not answer right away. She lay on her pillow, wondering if she had dreamed of the bright light and the angels. At first she thought she wouldn't say anything to her mother, because she would only say she was foolish and that her fever made her dream.

But she said, "Mother, last night I saw the most beautiful sight. The sky was lit up like thousands of twinkling stars, and I saw angels close to the earth and heard them singing, 'Glory to God in the highest, and on earth peace to men of good will.' Do you think the Saviour has really come at last?"

But before her mother could answer, her father burst into the room. He seemed excited and very happy.

"The Saviour has come!" he said. "I saw Him with my own eyes last night in a stable near Bethlehem. The most beautiful little Baby I ever laid eyes on. He lay on the straw beside His mother near the ox and the ass. His eyes were as blue as the sky; he had golden curls and a halo of light shone above His head!"

"You must have dreamed all this," said the mother.

"But I didn't!" the shepherd said. "While I was sitting in the field, watching the sheep, I saw a bright star that lit up the heavens all around me. And out of the light came an angel dressed in white garments. And the angel said, 'Fear not, for behold, I bring you good news of great joy. For unto you is born this night in the city of David, a Saviour who is Christ the Lord. And this shall be a sign unto you: You will find the Babe wrapped in swaddling clothes and lying in a manger.'"

The shepherd continued with the story, saying, "Above and around the angel came a host of other angels singing 'Glory to God in the highest.' And after a while the light faded and they were gone from the sky. And then other shepherds from the hillside came to me and said, 'What do you think of this miracle in the sky? Why are we chosen to be the first to learn of the Saviour's coming? We are but poor shepherds of the fields. Do you think it could be a mistake?'

"But I told them that we should go and worship our new Prince of Peace. And when we got to Bethlehem, we found Him in a stable near the town. The Child's father let us come inside, and each of us knelt down and touched the soft little fingers of the Child!"

"Oh, father," said Ruth, "I, too, saw the bright light and heard the angels singing. I knelt at the window last night and saw it all. But this morning I thought I must have dreamed the whole thing. Now I know it was real. Could I go to see the Holy Child and touch His little fingers?"

"Ruth, as soon as you are well," the old shepherd said, "you may go to the stable and see Him. I will give you a new baby lamb to take as a gift."

"But father," Ruth said, "I feel well this morning. The little Christ Child has made me well and strong again! Could I get up now?" And she didn't wait for an answer, but got out of her bed and danced around the room. "See," she said, "I am well. Now I can help you with the sheep and goats."

"It is amazing!" her mother said. "Only yesterday she seemed so sick, I thought she would be in bed for a long time. Praised be the little Saviour! The miracle last night has made my little one well again!"

After breakfast, Ruth was anxious to go to the fields with the sheep. She asked her mother to hurry and fix her lunch. Then, dressing warmly in her heaviest clothes, she hurried out to the sheep. She drove them to the place where her father had seen the angels. To her surprise, the ground all around her as far as she could see, was covered with sweet-smelling white blossoms! Such beautiful little flowers; each one was like a tiny star, its center a delicate green.

"Oh, what a lovely place," she thought, and she sat down in the field of blossoms. "The Christ Child has blessed the earth with flowers! God is good. He has made them to honor His little Son over in Bethlehem."

Ruth was never so happy in her whole life. She played in the field of flowers all day. But soon it would be getting dark, and she knew she must hurry home with the sheep.

Before she left the lovely field, she gathered her arms full of the little star flowers. She would take them home to show her father and mother what God had done to honor His Son. Her father would be pleased to know that she had picked them right where he had seen the angels last night.

Soon everyone in the village heard about the miracle flowers. They called them Stars of Bethlehem. Today, as at that time, the little star flowers grow in Palestine in the winter to honor the Saviour, and as a remembrance of the Star of Bethlehem.

THE CHRISTMAS ROSE

WHEN Jesus was born in the town of Bethlehem, Wise Men came from the east with gifts of gold, frankincense, and myrrh.

It was late afternoon, just before sundown, when the great caravan neared the city. The sight of the city just ahead made the Wise Men very happy because they had traveled many days and nights in search of the Holy One. But at last they reached their destination. They were eager to see the new Prince of Peace and present Him with the precious gifts they had brought. They were tired, too, and anxious to stop and rest. But first they must go into the city and inquire where the newborn King was.

"Soon the sun will be going down over the hills," said Melchior, "and darkness will be upon us. We must hurry and make camp."

And after seeing Herod at the palace, they returned to their camp just outside the walls of the city.

With their gifts in order, they set about changing from their dusty travel clothes into fresh cloaks and turbans. It would not do for the Wise Men of the East to be in the presence of the Mighty One in dirty clothes.

Nearby on the hillside, a little shepherd girl was busy caring for her father's sheep. There was a chill in the air; she shivered, and wrapped her coat more closely about her. She knew her father would be coming soon to relieve her and take over the night watch, and she must be ready for him. After making a fresh campfire, she rounded up all the sheep. And when all was ready, she rested and waited. In the distance near Bethlehem she saw the great caravan preparing to camp for the night.

"I wonder who they are, and why they are stopping here," she thought. Then she remembered the little Saviour of the world, born in the stable at Bethlehem. She said, "They must be coming to see the Holy Infant Jesus."

When her father came to take over the night watch, she did not go right home, but wandered over to ask another shepherd about the strange caravan.

"Kind sir," she said to the old man tending his flock near her own, "what do you make of the great caravan just outside the city?"

And the shepherd replied, "It is the Wise Men from the East. They have come to see the newborn King of the Jews and to worship Him. They have journeyed a long way, and are planning to give Him precious gifts from the Orient."

When the little shepherdess heard him say they had precious gifts, she knew she had to see them. And with hope in her heart, she hurried over to where the Wise Men were.

Shyly, she asked one of the Wise Men if she might see the rare and precious gifts they were bringing the little Saviour. "One of the shepherds told me you have traveled many miles to see the newborn King."

Melchior, the eldest of the Wise Men said, "You may see the gifts, child, but do not touch them. They are in order, for we will soon present them to the Holy One."

When the little girl saw the carved boxes of ebony and gold, she said, "Oh, how precious they are! The Infant Jesus will be so pleased."

And feeling very sad, she hurried away. She was very poor and had no gift to offer the little Jesus. More than anything else, she wanted to give Him a gift and see His lovely face.

"First the shepherds hurried to the manger with gifts. Now the Wise Men come with their precious treasures. Surely there is something I could take Him," she thought.

She prayed that she would soon have a gift to bring the little Jesus. But she felt so sad that she sat down on the ground and began to cry. As she was sobbing, she looked up to see an angel from heaven standing before her.

The angel said, "Little shepherdess, why do you weep?"

And the little girl answered, "The shepherds and the Wise Men have beautiful gifts for the little Saviour over in the stable at Bethlehem. I am sad because I have nothing to give Him."

But the angel told her, "Child, your love for the little Saviour is the best gift of all."

And as the little girl's tears fell to the ground, flowers sprang up before her! Beautiful white blossoms that were so lovely she could not believe what she saw.

"Oh, how pretty they are!" she cried. "I have never seen so many flowers."

She was so happy, she gathered all the flowers her little arms could hold, and hurried to the manger where Jesus was.

When she reached the stable, she asked if she might come in and present her gift to the little Babe. And

Mother Mary, seeing the little girl looking hopefully at her Son, said, "Come in, my child."

The little shepherdess knelt at the crib and held up the flowers so Jesus could see them.

"I pray that He will accept my gift," she said.

Her answer came, for as His little hands reached up to touch the flowers, He looked right at her and smiled so sweetly she knew He was pleased with her gift!

And so a new flower bloomed on that first Christmas. We call it the Christmas Rose. And to this day, the Christmas Rose blooms at Christmas time.

THE GRASS FLOWER

AT MIDNIGHT, in a field not far from the stable in Bethlehem, a shepherd named Joshua and his son Jonathan lay peacefully sleeping on the ground. All around them the goats and sheep were huddled together for warmth. It was quiet, except for the bleating of a baby lamb.

Suddenly the midnight sky before them lit up with a brightness that blotted out the other stars. The red, leaping flames of the shepherds' fire faded as the heavenly light shone down upon them.

The little shepherd boy was the first to awaken and notice the light. "Father, I'm afraid," he cried out, moving closer to his father. "What is it?"

At first his father was too amazed to say anything. "I have never seen such brightness," he said. "It lights up the whole world. It must be a miracle. Perhaps it is news of the coming of the Messias. God promised to send the world a Saviour, and the prophets said that a great brightness would shine around Him. Look, Jonathan, someone is coming."

And out of the golden light, a beautiful angel in white garments came and stood before them. They were frightened, and hid their faces.

But the angel spoke, and his voice quieted their fears. "Be not afraid," he said, "for behold I bring you good news of great joy which shall be to all people. For unto you is born this day, in the city of David, a Saviour, who is Christ the Lord!"

"Christ is born in Bethlehem!" said Joshua. "This is the good news!"

The angel continued, saying, "And this shall be a sign unto you: You will find the Infant wrapped in swaddling clothes and lying in a manger."

"But why should the Messias be born in a lowly manger?" Joshua asked. "He is the new Prince of Peace and should be born in a high place. I cannot understand it."

Jonathan and his father stood still, wondering. Then

around and above the angel there appeared still more angels, praising God and singing, "Glory to God in the highest, and on earth peace to men of good will."

The shepherds saw the whole countryside light up with the brightness of the angels. Over the flocks of sheep, over the fields and hills, over the city of Bethlehem they circled, close to earth, singing, "Glory to God in the highest."

And when they were gone, it was dark and the night was as before. For a time neither spoke, for they were filled with wonder and delight. Nothing like this had ever happened before.

"Father, tell me what all this means," Jonathan said. "I clearly heard the angel say that Christ was born in a manger in the city of David. Does that mean the Holy One who will free the world from sin is born in Bethlehem tonight?"

"You are right, my son," said Joshua. "It is the promised Messias. He is the new King of the Jews, the Prince of Peace. It is just as I have told you: There shall come forth a Mighty One among us, the Holy Redeemer, who shall be greater than all the kings of the world."

"Let us go," the father said, "and pick out a fine young lamb to take to the Christ Child as a gift. Then we will hurry to Bethlehem and see this miracle."

Soon Joshua and Jonathan were hurrying toward the stable. On the way they met other shepherds. Joshua and the shepherds talked about the miracle. They, too, were eager to go to Bethlehem and see the Holy Child. Joshua said, "My son and I are on our way to the manger. Come with us, and together we will worship Him."

Now at that time there were many caves among the hills in Palestine. They were used as stables for animals in the wintertime. When the shepherds came to the first cave near Bethlehem, all was quiet and dark inside. They hurried on, hoping to find the right cave. Near the town they found the owner of an inn taking care of some horses. The shepherds said, "The angel of the Lord came to us and said that the Saviour was born in a stable near Bethlehem. Is this the place?"

But the owner said, "There is no Saviour here. Can't you see how busy I am? Go away, foolish shepherds."

So they hurried away, and continued their search. They soon found the place.

Inside the cave, Mary lay awake beside Joseph, ready to take care of Jesus if He should wake up and cry. "Joseph, I hear talking outside," she said. "I am afraid. Go and see who is there, but be careful not to let any robbers in."

Outside, the shepherds were waiting for an answer to their knock. "I will knock again," said Joshua. "Perhaps they did not hear the first time."

But just as he was going to try again, a voice from inside said, "Who is there?"

"It is I, Joshua, my son, and some shepherds from the hills. An angel of the Lord came to us tonight and said that the Christ Child was born in a manger at Bethlehem. We have come to honor the newborn King of the Jews and present Him with the gifts we have brought."

Joseph was not afraid now. It was as God had planned. He unlocked the stable door and spoke quietly to the shepherds.

"Good evening," Joseph said. "You have come to the right place. The Baby Jesus is in the manger. We could not find a room at the inn. I will speak with my wife, Mary. If she is well enough you may come in. Wait here."

Inside, Joseph quickly went to where Mary and the Baby were. He said, "It is some shepherds, Mary, who say that an angel told them they would find our Baby in Bethlehem. They have come to honor Him with gifts. Shall I bring them in?"

"Tell them to come in," Mary said. "We will be glad to see them."

In the meantime, while Joshua was talking with the shepherds, Jonathan ran out into the fields nearby and gathered his arms full of clean grass. He did not have a gift for the Baby Jesus, and he thought this grass would be something soft for Him to sleep on. He ran back to his father and the shepherds, and just in time, too, for they were already going inside.

Joseph led the shepherds into the stable. He held up

an old lantern so they could see better. And there in the manger, near the ox and the ass, lay Jesus, King of the world, the most beautiful little Baby they had ever seen. His hair lay in tiny ringlets, his eyes were bright, and a golden light shone above His head.

The shepherds knelt and worshiped the newborn King. Then one by one, they offered the gifts they had brought: a new little baby lamb, a pair of white doves, and a coverlet of warm lamb's wool. Little Jonathan was the last to bring up his gift. He laid his clean grass near the little Saviour.

"What have you there, little one?" Mary asked.

And Jonathan said, "I did not have a fine gift for Jesus as my father and the shepherds had, so I went out into the fields and brought Him fresh grass for His manger bed."

Joshua was amazed at his son. He said, "That is not a nice gift for the newborn King of the world."

But Mary, seeing that Jonathan was beginning to cry, quickly said, "Jesus will be more comfortable lying on this clean, fresh grass. Thank you, little one."

So Mary asked Joseph to fix the bed of grass. And when Mary laid Jesus down, His little hands touched the grass and there appeared on every blade tiny pink blossoms! The blossoms filled the air in the cave with a delightful perfume.

Joshua and the shepherds were surprised to see the

lovely pink blossoms. But Jonathan was the happiest of all, for his gift to the little Saviour was the best of all.

"God be praised!" said Joshua. "Only He could do this thing."

To Jonathan Mary said, "This is my Son's way of thanking you for your gift."

And ever since that time, the grass flower blooms abundantly during the Christmas season in spite of the cold and frosty nights that so often come. It is a remembrance of the little shepherd boy's humble gift to the Saviour.

☆

☆

THE FLIGHT INTO EGYPT

☆

☆

AFTER the Wise Men had visited Jesus and had left for their own country, Mary and Joseph prepared to go to bed. Mary was very tired. As soon as Joseph had made her comfortable for the night, she quickly fell asleep.

Joseph lay down, too, but he was thinking of the happiness of the Wise Men and of the gifts they had brought. He did not know that an angel would tell the Wise Men to go home a different way, so that the wicked

King would not know where the Christ Child was.

When he had finally fallen asleep, Joseph was visited by an angel in a dream. The angel said to him, "Arise, Joseph, take the Child Jesus and His mother and flee into Egypt. Be there until I visit you again. For it will come to pass that Herod will seek the young Child to destroy Him." Then the angel left him. He awoke, sat up, and looked about him. Jesus and Mary were still all right.

Joseph was much troubled at the angel's warning. The King was already looking for the Child Jesus. Joseph would have to do something quickly.

"Mary," said Joseph, gently tapping her on the shoulder. "I must talk to you. An angel came to me and said that King Herod's soldiers were out to find Jesus and destroy Him. He said that we must hurry and flee into Egypt."

Mary was eager to leave when she heard Joseph's words. "Let us pack a few of our things and take the little donkey and hurry away," she said. "It is nighttime; no one will see us if we leave now."

"But Mary, I do not have enough money to travel so far," Joseph said sadly.

"We have the gifts the Wise Men left for Jesus," she said. "Wouldn't that be enough to help us buy food and lodging along the way?"

"Ah, yes, Mary," said Joseph happily. "The rare gifts will see us through. Thank God we have them!"

Soon Joseph had the little donkey outside, and Mary and Jesus were upon it. They quietly left their home and hurried out to the gates of the city. At the gate they were met by a guard. He said, "Stop! Who goes there?" Mary and Joseph were afraid. They must ask the guard to let them go on.

"It is only a poor man and his family leaving the city," Joseph said.

"Begone then," said the guard, angry that he had been awakened at this hour of the night.

So they hurried away from the city. And when they were far away, they stopped to rest. Mary said, "Joseph, I am glad we left Bethlehem when we did. Now we can travel without fear of the wicked soldiers."

But Mary did not know that Herod had given orders that no one should give food or shelter to them. For if they did, they would be put to death.

The Holy Family had now traveled many days in the hot desert wilderness. The little donkey's steps became slower and slower. Jesus was restless, and Mary and Joseph were tired and thirsty.

"Soon we will find water," said Joseph. He knew they could not last much longer in the desert without water.

In the distance Mary saw some palm trees. This meant

that an oasis was near. There would be water to drink, to bathe Jesus, and to do some cooking. There was hope now. "God is good, Joseph," Mary said. "See, just ahead is the oasis."

"Water at last!" Joseph said. And when they reached the pool, they drank from the cool water and were refreshed.

It was so nice at the oasis the Holy Family stayed longer than they had planned. Mary bathed Jesus several times, and washed his clothes. "How nice it is to be clean again, and away from the heat of the desert sun," she said.

While they were at the oasis, Joseph met a caravan going to Jerusalem. With the gold Jesus was given by the Wise Men, Joseph bought food for the rest of the journey. Once again all was right with them. They were ready to continue on their way. But Mary hated to leave the lovely spot where they had rested, and where Jesus had sat on her lap and played with the pretty desert flowers.

The Holy Family traveled on, and after a time in the desert they came to a camp. It was the winter camp of a group of men, women, and children who had been driven from their home. In the summer they traveled, picking up clothing, sheep, goats, and other animals. In the winter they made camp and lived on the provisions and food they had taken from their travels.

It was dark when Mary and Joseph entered the camp. Joseph said to the Chief, "My wife and Child are weary from the long journey in the desert. We can go no farther without food and drink. We beg your mercy, and ask that you let us stay until tomorrow."

The Chief looked at Joseph, and then at the sweet-faced mother holding her little Child. He saw the tired-ness in her eyes, and the hunger in her cheeks. He saw the glowing light that shone above the Child's head. He knew this was the family from Bethlehem that was fleeing from King Herod.

"You are the family from Bethlehem, and the Child is the Holy Child called the Prince of Peace," said the Chief. "Do you not know that the King's messengers have said that he who shelters the family from Bethlehem shall be put to death?" And he went into the tent to talk with the other members of the clan.

Soon he returned, and said to Mary and Joseph, "You may stay with us. We care not what the wicked King Herod says. You are welcome." And he gave orders that food and wine be brought to them at once.

That night Mary and Joseph slept on soft animal skins by the campfire. Jesus was well cared for. The leader had begun to love the little boy with the sweet smile and golden curls. He gave Him gold bracelets and other jewelry to play with.

The next morning the Holy Family was well rested and ready to leave. They thanked the Chief for his kind-ness and gifts.

"We were happy to have you with us," said the Chief, "and pleased to help the Child Jesus on His way into Egypt. A safe journey to you!"

One day, there was a sandstorm in the desert, and the sand was blowing in their faces.

"Joseph," said Mary, "we must find shelter soon. The sand has almost blinded me, and Jesus is very restless." And with loving care, she wrapped her shawl about Jesus, and pulled her own scarf over her face. But Joseph could not cover his face; he had to lead the donkey.

As Mary sat on the donkey's back, she could not help remembering the lovely oasis and wishing she could be there. But God had commanded them to go to Egypt, and they must obey His wishes.

The storm grew worse; the wind was blowing harder now. Joseph's face was swollen and cracked. The water in the bottle was fast disappearing for they drank more and more. The sandstorm made their throats dry and parched. The donkey drank more too, and Joseph had to ration it. It was getting very low, and he did not know when they would reach a well.

Joseph stopped the donkey and prepared a kind of tent to keep out the sand and wind. They could not keep on in such a storm. He turned the little animal to the side and threw a blanket over him so that it reached the ground. Then he and Jesus and Mary got under the blanket and waited for the storm to quiet itself. When the storm was over, the sand had piled up almost to the top of the donkey.

"This is hard for you, Mary," said Joseph. "It is too bad that you have to suffer so. But we must go on, for it is God's will."

When they had traveled a few more miles, they reached another oasis. Here was water and they could rest. They were grateful for the fruit on the trees. They stayed several days. But just as they were ready to leave, they were surprised by a band of robbers who took the clothing and fruit they had packed for the rest of the trip. They took the remaining gold that Joseph had in his pocket. When they had taken all they wanted, they ran away, laughing at their prize! Sadly Mary and Joseph sat down and repacked fruit. They still had the myrrh and frankincense, and the clothes on their backs. And after filling their water bottles, they left the oasis.

The journey grew harder and harder to bear, in spite of their rest at the oasis. The hot sun was beating down on them. Mary's eyes hurt her. By nighttime she was completely exhausted. Joseph, too, was blinded by the rays of the sun on the desert sands.

"I wonder if we will ever reach Egypt?" Joseph said. "It seems so very far away."

"God will help us, Joseph," Mary said.

On and on they traveled, passing skeletons of animals that had died for lack of water. It made Mary and Joseph sad, for they knew it was hard to live in the desert. If they did not find water soon, they too might not be able to go on. There was less and less food now, and the sun exhausted them. But at last, after several days, they reached a village. Their joy was great when they saw the huts and fountains, and rows and rows of palm trees swaying in the breeze. Mary thought she had never seen a more beautiful sight. Here and there flowers bloomed, and she stopped to pick some for Jesus. And when they neared the village, little children ran out to meet them. "What is your name?" they asked eagerly.

"My name is Mary, and Joseph is my husband," Mary answered. "And this is my Son, Jesus." And she proudly held Him up so they could see Him.

At the well inside the village they drank and were refreshed. The people were kind to them, and gave them food and clothing.

It was weeks since they had left Bethlehem, but to Mary it seemed like years. Time passed quickly now. Jesus learned to talk and walk. He played happily with the other children of the village. Mary and Joseph were content and happy, too, because Jesus was such a joy to them.

But they knew this was not Egypt. God had said they must go there to be safe. So once again they prepared to leave. When they rode out into the desert, Mary was very sad. She left many friends behind, and she knew they must face many more hardships on the journey ahead.

There were many lions and other wild animals in the desert. Joseph watched carefully that they did not attack or hurt Jesus and Mary. He knew the animals were often hungry and looking for food of any kind. Sometimes the animals came close to them, but they always ran away, as if some powerful force were after them.

After many days of travel, Joseph grew worried that they had become lost. He was certain they should now be in Egypt. But he did not say anything to Mary; it would only worry her more. Joseph noticed a strange gleam in her eyes and he knew this showed how very tired she was. With all his heart, he hoped they would reach a village or an oasis soon. They had no water and their food was almost gone.

"Soon we will find some water, Mary," Joseph said, trying hard to be cheerful for her sake. "We should be in Egypt before very long. I am sure we will find a place to rest there." But Mary just sat silent. After a while she said, "God will help us. He has been good to us on the long journey."

In the distance they saw palm trees, and were again hopeful. They hurried to find the water. But when they reached the spot, they found that the well was dry! And the fruit was so high on the trees that Joseph could not reach it. Mary was completely worn out. She laid the Child Jesus down and seated herself on the dry earth. Joseph flung himself down beside her and pressed his face against hers.

"We must pray as we have never prayed before," Mary said. And they did.

Then Jesus awoke. Now Jesus is God's Son and God can do anything. God knew that Mary and Joseph were in great need. He had followed them through the desert, and had guardian angels watch over them all the way.

So Jesus went over to a tree and looked up at the fruit. And the fruit dropped to the earth at His feet! And He went over to the well, and at once it was full of cool water! The Holy Family ate and drank and, after a while, rested beneath the tree.

"God is good," Mary said. And all was well again. They prayed together, and thanked God for saving their lives. Soon they were rested and on their way.

After several more days they were in Egypt. Mary set up housekeeping. Joseph found work as a carpenter. Jesus grew and became a fine young boy.

They lived in Egypt until the angel of the Lord came to Joseph in a dream and said, "Arise and take the Child and His mother and go back into the land of Israel. For they are dead that sought the young Child's life."

The Holy Family left Egypt for their home in Nazareth. And it was as God said: "Out of Egypt I called My Son."

☆
☆

THE OTHER WISE MAN*

☆

☆

IN THE days when Augustus Caesar was master of kings, and Herod was ruler of Jerusalem, there lived in the city of Ecbatana, in Persia, a man named Artaban. His house stood close to the walls of the royal treasury. From his roof top he could look out over the land and view the horizon. Around his home there were fair gardens, beautiful flowers, and fruit trees that were watered by the streams from the mountains.

* Adapted from *The Other Wise Man,* by Henry Van Dyke.

On this September night, only a glow of light could be seen from the windows of Artaban's home where he was holding a meeting with his friends, the scholars of the Zoroaster.

Artaban was a tall, dark man of forty years, with deep-set eyes under a heavy brow. He had the appearance of a dreamer, but the build of a soldier. He wore a robe of pure white wool over a tunic of silk; a white cap rested on his black hair. He was dressed like the ancient priests of the Magi, the fire worshipers of Zoroaster.

From the doorway of his house, he greeted his guests. "Welcome," he said, "and peace be with you Abdus, Rhodaspes, and Tigranes, and with you, my father Abgarus. I am glad to see you."

The men were dressed in robes of richly colored silks, with golden collars about their necks, the dress of nobles and followers of the Zoroaster. Each man took his place around the altar where a tiny flame was burning. Artaban made the fire glow brighter, and they chanted the hymn of their worship. When the song was ended, Artaban asked his friends to be seated at the table so they could continue with the meeting.

"You have come here tonight," said Artaban, "to renew your worship and rekindle your faith in God. We worship not the fire, but Him who is the symbol of light and truth."

"I will tell you, my father and friends," he continued,

"about a new light and truth which has come to me through the ancient signs of the sky. We of the Magi have read many books of prophecy and studied many signs of fire and water. The highest of all our learning is the knowledge of the stars. Is it not so, my friends?"

And Tigranes answered, saying, "The stars are numberless. The wisdom of the Magi is the greatest of all wisdoms on earth. This is the secret of power. We keep men looking and waiting for the new sunrise."

"The books tell us that in time all men will one day see the brightness of a great light," said Artaban.

"That is true," said Abgarus, Artaban's father. "Every faithful disciple of Zoroaster knows of the prophecy: One day the Victorious One shall arise out of the number of prophets. Around Him shall shine a mighty brightness, and He shall make life everlasting, and the dead shall rise again."

"It may be that we will never understand it," said Tigranes. "It is better that we consider the things at hand, rather than look for one who may be a stranger."

Then Artaban drew two rolls of paper from his tunic and unfolded them. He said, "We have read of the prophecy of the wise old man named Balaam who said: There shall come a star out of Jacob, and a scepter shall arise out of Israel."

And Tigranes said, "The tribes of Israel are scattered over the lands, and all who dwell in Judea are under the strict rule of the Romans; neither star not scepter shall arise."

But Artaban said, "Do you not remember the prophecy of the Hebrew Daniel? It reads: Know therefore, and understand that from the going forth of the commandment to restore Jerusalem, unto the Anointed One, the Prince, the time shall be seven and threescore and two weeks."

"But my son," said Abgarus, "these are but mystical numbers. We know not how to find their meaning."

And Artaban said, "It has been shown to me and to my three companions among the Magi, Casper, Melchior, and Balthazar. We have searched the ancient tablets of Chaldea and know the time. It falls in this year. We have studied the sky, and in the spring of the year we saw two great planets draw together in the sign of the Fish, which is the house of the Hebrews. We also saw a bright new star which shone for one night and then vanished. Now again the two great planets are meeting. My brothers of the Magi are watching at the Temple of the Seven Spheres in Babylon, and I am watching here. If the star shines again, they will wait ten days for me at the Temple, and then we will set out for Jerusalem, to see and worship the new King of Israel."

The scholars were astonished when Artaban told them he had made ready for the journey, and that he had sold all his possessions. From his tunic he brought out jewels and laid them on the table. "I have bought three jewels, a sapphire, a ruby, and a pearl, to give to the King when I find Him. I ask you, my friends, to go with me on the pilgrimage that we may have joy together and find the Prince of Peace."

But the scholars were doubtful of the trip and shook their heads. They thought Artaban was foolish to give up everything for a strange adventure such as this.

Tigranes said, "Artaban, this is an empty dream. It comes from too much looking at the stars. You would be wiser to stay and spend your time gathering money for the new fire temple. No king will ever arise from Israel. But if you must go, farewell."

Another said, "I am guardian of the royal treasury, and cannot go. But if you have planned to go, I bid you farewell."

And another said, "I cannot leave my new bride for a strange adventure. It is not for me to go. So farewell, Artaban."

One by one they left the house of Artaban. Only Abgarus, the oldest, lingered to talk to Artaban. "My son, it may be that the light of truth in the skies will lead you to the Prince of Peace. It may also be that you will search in vain. I am too old to go with you, but my heart will go with you on the journey and be your companion. Go in peace."

When Abgarus left, Artaban went out on the terrace

and watched the skies. As he was standing there, he saw the strange, bright star in the heavens. It shone like a precious jewel.

"It is the sign!" he said. "The King is coming, and I will go to meet Him."

All night long, Vasda, the swiftest of his horses, was saddled and bridled, ready for the journey. Before dawn, Artaban was in the saddle and riding westward along the base of Mount Orontes. He stopped to drink at a wayside spring and refresh his horse. Before going on, he prayed that all would go well on the journey. He knew he must hurry on to keep the appointment with the other Magi. It was still a long way, and he could not travel more than fifty miles each day. So he rode away swiftly.

He passed Mount Orontes, crossed the plains of Nicaea, and the fertile fields of Concabar. At Baghistan, he saw the figure of King Darius in his beautiful gardens. Over many a cold and desolate pass he rode, through mountain gorges, across fertile valleys, past cities, rivers, and rice fields. After passing the large cities of Ctesiphon and Seleucia, he crossed the Tigris and Euphrates rivers until, at nightfall on the tenth day, he reached the walls of Babylon.

Vasda was tired, but Artaban drove him on. It was only a three hours' journey to the Temple of the Seven Spheres where his friends were waiting for him. So he did not stop.

But Artaban could not continue as fast as he wanted to. His horse suddenly pulled up short and stopped, as if afraid. Artaban knew something was wrong. He got off his horse and looked about him. In the dim starlight, he saw the form of a man lying across the road. His face was haggard and his clothes dirty. His skin was dry and yellow, a sign of deadly fever. Artaban took his hand. There seemed to be no life in the man, as he lay motionless on the desert sand.

So Artaban turned away; but just as he was leaving, a moan came from the lips of the dying man. His bony fingers gripped Artaban's robe and held it fast.

Artaban felt sad; if he stayed to help the man, he would not reach his destination in time. The others would go on without him to find the Holy One. His trip would be in vain. But if he left the man, he would surely die. "Oh, God of truth," he prayed, "show me the way with Thy wisdom!"

Artaban knew he must help the poor fellow. He carried him to the shade of a palm tree and gave him drink and medicine that he carried with him. Hour after hour he worked to heal the man. At last, the man's strength returned and he could sit up.

"Who are you?" he said. "And why have you brought me back to life?"

"I am Artaban, the Magian. I am going to Jerusalem in search of the new King of the Jews. I cannot delay, for the other Wise Men will depart without me. But I will leave you food and drink."

"I have nothing to give you for your kindness," the man said. "But I can tell you that the Holy One will not be born in Jerusalem, but in Bethlehem of Judea. May the Lord take you safely to Him, because you have shown pity to the sick."

It was now past midnight. Artaban rode swiftly because he was late. When he reached the Temple of the Seven Spheres, he could not find his friends. There was no sign of the caravan!

But at the Temple he found a note from his friends that read: "We have waited past the midnight and can delay no longer. We go to find the King. Follow us across the desert."

In despair, Artaban sat down and covered his head with his hands. "How can I cross the desert," he thought, "with no food and a tired horse? I must sell the sapphire that I had saved for my King. I will have to return to Babylon and buy camels and food for the rest of the journey."

When all was again ready, Artaban rode out of the city of Babylon into the desert. All around him lay waste and death. In the hot dry desert he passed no living creatures except lions, jackals, and lizards. But through the heat and cold he moved on steadily.

Soon he reached Damascus, the beautiful city of gardens and orchards, the thickets of myrrh and roses. He passed into the fertile valley of the Jordan and into the plains of Esdraelon, until he reached Bethlehem. It was the third day after his friends had come to Bethlehem and found Mary and Joseph and the Child Jesus, and presented Him with gifts.

Artaban drew near the town, full of hope, with his ruby and pearl to offer the King. "This is the place the prophets said the King would be born."

The streets seemed deserted. From the open door of a cottage, he heard the sound of a woman's voice singing softly. He knocked and entered and found a young mother singing her baby to sleep. She greeted him and told him the other Wise Men had appeared in the village three days ago. They said that a star had guided them to where Mary and Joseph and the Infant Jesus were. And that they worshiped Him, and left rare gifts.

"But the Wise Men left suddenly," she said. "We in the village could not understand why. Joseph of Nazareth took the Child and His mother and fled into the night. It is said they went to Egypt."

The young mother's child touched the robe of Artaban, and he looked down at the sweet child. "Why could not this child have been the promised King that I have been searching for?" he thought. But he knew God had not yet rewarded him in his search. "The one I seek has gone," he said. "I must follow Him to Egypt."

The young mother gave him food and he was refreshed.

But just as he was about to leave, there came loud noises from the street, the sound of swords clashing and women crying. The young mother looked out the window. "The soldiers of Herod! They are killing the children!" she cried. And she picked up her child, covered him with a blanket, and went to the darkest corner of the room.

Artaban felt sorry for the young mother, and went to the door. The soldiers came, but Artaban stood in the doorway and would not let the Captain pass into the room.

"I am a peaceful man and do not wish to be disturbed. I will give this ruby to the Captain who will leave me in peace."

The Captain was eager to have the beautiful ruby. He took it and told the soldiers to go on.

Artaban had given away another of the gifts he had saved for the King of Israel. But he was not sorry, for he had seen great joy on the young mother's face.

"Because you have saved the life of my little one," the mother said, "may the Lord bless you and keep you; the Lord make His face to shine upon you and be gracious unto you; the Lord lift up His countenance upon you and give you peace."

So once again Artaban set out in search of the Saviour. He journeyed into Egypt, but looked in vain throughout the land. He searched among the rich and the poor, but could not find the Holy One. Unhappy, he returned to Jerusalem.

Thirty-three years he had looked for the Saviour! He was now an old man. His hair was no longer black, but white as snow. He was weary and ready to die, but still looking for the King.

It was the season of the Passover. There were many people in the city who had come for the great religious feast. Artaban asked some people the cause of the excitement in the city.

They answered, "We are going to the place called Golgotha, just outside the walls of the city, to see two robbers and a man named Jesus of Nazareth hanged on the cross. The man calls Himself the Son of God, and Pilate has sent Him to be crucified because He says He is the King of the Jews."

Artaban was astonished at these words, and thought, "At last I have found my King! The ways of God are stranger than the thoughts of men. It may be that I shall come in time to offer my pearl for His ransom before He dies!"

So Artaban walked as quickly as he could to the gates of the city. At the entrance he saw soldiers dragging a young girl down the street. Artaban felt great pity for the girl. But when she saw Artaban in his royal robes, she threw herself at his feet. "Have pity on me, save me!" she cried. So Artaban gave the girl his pearl, the last of the treasures he had saved for the King. "This, my daughter, is your ransom," he said.

As he spoke, darkness fell over the land, and the earth shook. The walls of the houses rocked, and great stones fell and crashed into the streets. A heavy stone fell upon Artaban and almost crushed his head. He lay dying in the arms of the girl he had helped.

As she bent over him, there came a voice from heaven, and she heard Artaban saying, "Three and thirty years I looked for Thee, Lord, but I have never seen Thy face, nor ministered to Thee!"

And the voice from heaven was saying, "Inasmuch as you did it to one of the least of My brethren, you did it to Me."

Artaban's face grew calm and peaceful. His long journey was ended. He had found his King!

THE MIRACLE THORN

IT HAPPENED, on Christmas day, many years after the crucifixion of our Lord on Calvary, that Joseph of Arimathea and a band of Christian pilgrims set sail from the Holy Land for England.

But for a time before the journey, Joseph had been in prison. The cruel Romans thought he had stolen our Lord's body from its tomb. But he had not, for our Lord arose from the dead on the third day after His burial.

Many times while in prison Joseph would pray, and his room would be filled with a glorious light and Jesus would appear to him and comfort him. The Romans wanted to put him to death, but when they went to the prison to get him he was gone! Someone had helped him escape. The King could not understand how it happened, because the room had neither a door nor a window.

In a small ship, Joseph and his pilgrims sailed out into the Mediterranean Sea. For a long time they traveled the sea route of the Roman merchant ships to England. Joseph carried with him the precious Holy Cup used by our Lord at the Last Supper.

It was a cold wintry day when the pilgrims landed on the coast of England. The trees which covered the plains were bare and leafless. A strong wind was blowing from the west, and gray clouds hung low over the earth. A deep river ran through the marshland. To the east was a high hill which was later called the Tor of Glastonbury.

Joseph led the way. He was an old man now, with white hair and beard. But he was young in spirit and a good leader. Those that knew him called him a good and holy man. He was a true disciple of Christ. Before going on shore, they stopped to pray and to thank God for the many blessings they had received.

The first day of the journey was very hard; they had

to go through swampy lands and forests. When night came they were too tired to go on, so they rested on Glastonbury Hill. From this point they could look around the country and see where they had to go.

"It is a pretty country," said Joseph. "I like the woods and hills, the wide rivers and grassy marshlands. I would like to live here. What do the rest of you say?"

"It is a fine country," said one of the pilgrims, "but let us eat first and get some rest."

As they ate, they talked about their long journey from Palestine to this strange land where they hoped to stay. Until now they had been by themselves and had not seen any natives. But at twilight a group of heathen natives, armed with weapons, came toward the small group on the hillside. The pilgrims were startled and did not have time to run for cover. So Joseph told them to kneel in prayer, for they would not be able to escape.

Joseph plunged his staff into the ground and looked toward heaven, asking God to help them. "Merciful God, we have suffered long. Save us!"

The heathen natives stopped in their tracks, for the staff that Joseph had planted in the ground had suddenly grown into a thorn tree, with branches and green leaves! The buds became beautiful white blossoms that filled the air with perfume!

God had answered Joseph's prayer. This was a sign

that God wanted them to stay in this land, free from the wicked Romans. Joseph was pleased.

At the sight of the wonderful tree, the natives dropped their swords and hurried away. They were too frightened to go on with plans of killing the Christian pilgrims.

But news of the happenings on Glastonbury Hill spread far and wide over the land. The heathen King asked to see the man who had caused the miracle blooming of the staff. And when he saw Joseph, he gave him the valley of Avalon, a beautiful spot where he could live in peace.

Here in the valley of Avalon, Joseph and the pilgrims built little houses from twigs and reeds from the marsh. Here, too, Joseph built a small church. In the church, Joseph taught the heathen natives all about Christ and the truths of the faith. He made many converts.

The children were the most eager to hear the stories about the Christ Child. "What was the little Christ Child like?" they asked him. And Joseph replied, "He was the most beautiful little Baby in the world! He was born in a stable in Bethlehem. God sent His Son to free the world from sin. I was but a young child when I went with my father to see Him in the manger. When He grew into manhood, I heard Him preach the lessons of love to the people."

Joseph never tired of telling the people about Christ. One day he said to his followers, "I was at Calvary and saw my Lord led up the hill to Golgotha. I saw Him crucified and die on the cross. After He died, I placed His holy body in a tomb. After three days He arose from the dead, just as He said He would. The wicked Romans thought I had stolen His body from the tomb, and put me in prison. But I had not. Later, with the help of my friends, I escaped and fled to this fair land of England."

All who heard Joseph believed. And after many years he died. A new large Abbey was built in honor of the holy man from Palestine.

Today, people all over the world come to see the ruins of the once beautiful Abbey that was destroyed by a wicked king who did not believe in God. And they walk in the grounds where Joseph buried the Holy Cup of our Lord. And they come to watch the budding of the miracle thorn that blooms every year at Christmas time, a sign of God's everlasting love.

☆
☆

THE GOOD ST. NICHOLAS*

☆
☆

A LONG, long time ago, in the fourth century, there
lived a famous and holy man named Nicholas. His
name, which means victory, was given him because he
helped people overcome their sins by showing them
good example. He was a true man of God, charitable
and kind. All he did was for his God in heaven. It was
his belief that only through giving to others could he

* Adapted from *The Golden Legend* of Jacobus de Voragine, translated by
Ryan and Ripperger, published by Longmans, Green and Co.

deserve God's everlasting love, and get to heaven. He was loved and praised by all who knew him, and he had power to make all things bright and clean.

As a young boy, Nicholas lived with his father Epiphanius, and his mother Joanna. His parents were rich, but they loved God very much.

When other boys were out playing, Nicholas spent his time visiting and praying in the churches. He read the Bible many times and memorized its pages. And when his father and mother died, he was left a great amount of money. But he spent it wisely, for he used his wealth to promote God's glory by helping others.

It was Nicholas who started the custom of hanging up the stocking at Christmas time. One of his neighbors, a poor man of noble birth, needed money badly in order to have his three daughters married properly. Nicholas heard of this and decided to help the man. He wrapped up a lump of gold in a cloth and went to the man's house after dark. He threw the lump of gold through the window. It landed in the stocking of the eldest daughter.

In the morning the daughter discovered the gold and the poor widower prepared at once for her wedding.

Some time later, Nicholas did the same thing a second time. When the gold was found, the poor neighbor was very pleased and this time he decided to watch for the one who gave the gold.

A few days later, Nicholas threw an even larger piece

of gold into the stocking of the youngest daughter. The
noise of the gold hitting the floor told the poor man that
his visitor was outside. So he ran after Nicholas, who had
started away, and begged him to stop so he could see his
face. He ran faster than Nicholas and caught up with
him. Over and over the poor man thanked him, but
Nicholas did not want to be thanked. He asked the man
to keep it a secret all his life.

Sometime afterward, the Bishop of the city of Myra
died, and all the bishops of the region gathered to choose
his successor. Among the group was a certain Bishop of
great authority. The great Bishop told them all to fast
and pray that they would find a good and holy man for
the office of bishop.

It was that night that the great Bishop heard a voice
telling him to go to the door of the church in the early
hours of the morning and wait there. The man who first
entered the church, whose name was Nicholas, was the
man for the important office of Bishop of Myra.

Meanwhile, Nicholas went to the church before dawn
and was the first to enter. The Bishop, who was waiting
at the door, came up to him and asked, "What is your
name, good man?" Nicholas bowed his head and said, "I
am Nicholas, servant of Your Holiness." Then the Bishop
led him into the church and made him the new Bishop
of Myra.

Nicholas was greatly pleased with his new office, and

spent the rest of the day in prayer and fasting. He knew he needed God's guidance to be a good bishop. He felt that by much prayer and by giving up his gold, he could deserve the important office that he had.

One day a certain group of seamen were caught in a great storm that threatened to take their lives, so they prayed to Nicholas for help. They said, "Nicholas, servant of God, help us as you have helped so many others."

Suddenly a stranger appeared on board the ship and said to them, "You called me, here I am." And he began at once to help them with the sails and ropes. And the storm went away.

After they had landed safely, the men went to the church where Nicholas was and recognized him as the man on the ship who had helped them. They thanked him, but Nicholas said, "Do not thank me, but your God in heaven. It was your faith that saved you."

Another time there was a great famine in the diocese, and the people had nothing left to eat. Nicholas heard that a ship loaded with grain was anchored in the harbor. He went at once to the master of the ship and asked for help for his starving people.

But the master replied, "Good Nicholas, we dare not take out any of this grain for it has all been measured. If we took some out, we would be severely punished."

And Nicholas said, "I promise you in God's name that the amount you take out will not be noticed." So they took away a great quantity of the grain which Nicholas gave to his people. It was enough to feed all of them for two years, with some left over for planting.

When the men on the ship reached their destination, they noticed the shipment was as if it had not been touched. They saw the miracle, and praised God in the name of the good Nicholas.

One day Nicholas heard of three princes that were captured and about to be put to death for a crime they did not commit. He hurried to the place of execution and found the three on their knees, their heads covered and waiting to be killed. Nicholas took the sword away from the executioner, untied the three innocent men, and led them away. Later the Emperor found the three princes and put them back in jail, and ordered them to be put to death that very night. The three men remembered Nicholas and prayed to him, "O Nicholas, servant of God, come to our aid and save us from death."

That night, Nicholas, in answer to their prayer, came to the Emperor while he was sleeping and said, "Why have you arrested the three men again and condemned them to death when they are innocent? Get up quickly and order them to be set free. Otherwise I shall pray to God to stir up a war in which you shall be killed."

"Who are you, to come and talk to me in this way?" the Emperor asked.

And he said, "I am Nicholas, Bishop of Myra."

Then Nicholas went to the jailer and said, "Why have you jailed three innocent men? Go at once and release them. Otherwise your body will be eaten up by worms and your house destroyed!"

And the jailer said, "Who are you, to threaten me this way?"

And Nicholas replied, "I am Nicholas, Bishop of Myra."

Next morning the Emperor went to the jail and asked the three young men, "Do you know a man named Nicholas?"

The three men said they did, and that they had been praying to him for help. So the Emperor let them go. But first he said to them, "Go and thank the God who saved you because of the prayers of Nicholas. And tell him not to threaten me, but pray to God for me and for my empire."

Days later, the three princes visited Nicholas and told him all the Emperor had said. They thanked Nicholas for saving them. But Nicholas told them to thank God, not him. And he gave them instructions in the truths of the faith.

Nicholas died in the year 343. He was buried in a marble tomb, and a fountain of oil began to flow from his head, and a fountain of water from his feet. Even today, it is said, a holy oil comes from his bones and cures all sicknesses.

Many miracles came about through prayers and devotion of Nicholas. Many who saw the miracles were baptized and converted to the faith.

One time a man was brought back to life by the merits of Nicholas. Another time a man put a statue of Nicholas in his home to protect his belongings while he was away. Through the faith of a certain nobleman, his son who was harmed and killed by the Devil was restored to life.

A certain rich man prayed earnestly to Nicholas to bring him a son. And when the son was born, the man was so pleased he built a chapel in honor of Nicholas, and solemnly celebrated his feast every year. But one day the young man was captured and carried off into slavery.

On St. Nicholas Day, the young boy began to weep. The King asked why he cried so bitterly. And the boy said, "It was St. Nicholas who brought so much happiness to my parents. My father built a shrine for him. Today is his feast day, and I remember and pray to him to set me free."

The King said, "Your Nicholas can try to save you, but you will still remain my slave."

But at that very instant, the wind arose and destroyed the King's palace. It picked up the boy and carried him to the chapel where his parents were celebrating the feast of St. Nicholas.

Today, as for centuries, children all over the world remember this kindly Saint on December 6, which is his feast day. Children in several countries of Europe receive gifts from him on that day. He returns every year on St. Nicholas Eve bringing gifts to good children and switches to bad ones. In the morning they hurry downstairs to find chairs tipped over and misplaced, and the house in disorder. This shows them St. Nicholas visited them.

In America, children observe St. Nicholas Eve in a similar way. The good Saint, dressed in a white robe and carrying a bishop's staff and miter, leaves pennies or candy for good children. But it is on Christmas day, after the morning Mass, that American children receive their real presents that were brought by the Christ Child the night before.

☆
☆

BONIFACE AND THE HOLY TREE

☆

☆

IN THE forests of northern Europe there lived pagan, war-like tribes who worshiped false gods. Each year, on the day of the winter sun festival and just before Christmas, they gathered around a great tree called the "thunder oak." Dressed in skins of wild animals, the men, women, and children met to honor their god Thor. It was the custom that a living child be sacrificed beneath this great oak.

A young priest from England, Boniface, who is now a

saint, heard about this cruel practice of sacrificing a little child to the god Thor. He decided to go to this northern province and put a stop to it.

Now Boniface, a tall but not large priest, was full of love for his fellow men. He was strong of will and knew no fear. He loved his brothers everywhere, and wanted everyone to know and love God and serve Him faithfully. Wherever he went, he spread the teachings of God and baptized many. He was most eager to go to Germany and teach the heathens the ways of Christian living.

But Boniface first had to go to Rome to get permission from the Pope. The Pope received Boniface and gave him permission to convert the heathens of northern Germany and to set up missions there. While in Rome, the Pope honored Boniface for his work, and gave him many blessings.

Upon returning home, Boniface got together a band of Christian men to accompany him on his journey. They were men of the forest and servants who were used to rough and hard work. For they must carry axes to cut away trees from the dense forests which, here and there, would block their way. They must carry bows and arrows and shooting weapons, because in those days the forests were filled with wild animals. Even worse than these were the outlaws and robbers that roamed the forests. This was not a small adventure, but a long and hard one.

On a day before Christmas, Boniface set sail with

his friends. He carried with him his staff and the cross of Christ.

It was a long journey, and many of the pilgrims grew tired and discouraged and wanted to turn back. But Boniface urged them to stay with him. Soon they left the ship and were walking inland through the forests of northern Germany. And leading the band of pilgrims was the priest who knew no fear.

On and on they traveled through the dense forests of northern and central Germany. The going was rough, and they had to endure many hardships and much suffering. But Boniface kept urging them forward. The forest seemed endless. They were now completely surrounded by nothing but trees which had to be cut down to make a path. But here and there would be a river or creek and an open road of sorts where they could make time on the journey.

Darkness came quickly, and the men were often tired and cold. There were deep drifts of snow, for this was a hard winter. The sun, for a time bright, quickly dropped behind the treetops.

"Good Boniface, let us rest and eat now," said one of the men. But Boniface was nearing his goal and urged them on.

"Have courage, my brothers," he said. "I know you are weary. I, too, am tired. But we have work to do. This is Christmas Eve, and there will be another human sacrifice at the gathering of the oak tree. We must hurry and show these pagans the Christian way to celebrate Christmas Eve. It is the birthnight of the Saviour of all. We are sent to help them worship Him, not to live in the darkness of pagan gods. Forward, my brothers!"

And so they traveled on, and after a while the road began to widen out a little. There were spaces of meadowland, which meant that they would soon be at their destination. In the distance they could see the great "thunder oak." It was so large, it stood high above the other trees in the forest. The pilgrims grew more hopeful now, and hurried on their way.

"Here in this forest, the cross of Christ will change the sinful ways of the pagans," said Boniface.

They could see the people at the gathering. At the foot of the tree a great fire was burning. Boniface and his men came up to the gathering.

"My brothers of the forest," said Boniface, "we need the comfort of your fire. We are tired and weary from our journey."

"Who are you," asked the leader, "and why have you come to us?"

And Boniface replied, "We are your Christian brothers, and have come from England, across the water. We bring you a message from our Saviour."

At first the leader did not want to welcome them. But then he said, "You may stay and watch the sacrifice. We must make a sacrifice to the god Thor for whom this great oak tree is sacred. See, we have picked a fine young son to be our offering."

And bravely kneeling before the sacred oak was a small boy. The leader picked up a huge ax and swung it above the young boy's head. But just at that moment, Boniface stepped forward and cried out, "No, my brothers, no blood shall be shed here tonight." And he raised the gleaming cross of Christ and said, "This is the birthnight of the Saviour of all mankind."

At the sight of the cross, the blow was turned aside, and the life of the frightened boy was spared. And at the same instant, the mighty oak tree fell crashing to the ground! The pagans were so frightened, they could hardly move to get out of the way of the falling tree.

Near the fallen oak, stood a young fir tree. Boniface pointed to the tree and said, "This tree shall be your holy tree tonight. See, its leaves are ever green, a sign of endless life. Let this be the holy tree of the Christ Child. Gather around it in your homes at Christmas time. Cover it with lights and gifts of loving kindness."

Boniface then told the people the story of the first Christmas, the sweet little Baby Jesus in the manger at Bethlehem, the shepherds, the angels, and the Wise Men who came to adore Him. They listened to his every word.

Everyone was happy that night. But the happiest of all was the mother who had her little son safe with her again. "The Saviour has helped me this night," she thought. And everyone rejoiced and went home with happy hearts. They found a new leader in Boniface. He would teach them to be Christians.

From that day until now, the fir tree has been used in homes on Christmas to celebrate the Saviour's birth, and to gladden the hearts of little children everywhere.

THE FIRST CHRISTMAS CRIB

A LONG time ago in the year 1223, Francis of Assisi, who is now called St. Francis, wanted all the people to have a greater love for God. At that time, most of the people were unable to read and had but few books. So the priests gathered them together as often as possible to tell them about God and the truths of the faith. Many people had far to go to attend Mass and the services of the church. Francis wanted everyone to know and love God and serve Him faithfully.

Because he was so good and kind, he was trusted and loved by everyone in and around the tiny village of Greccio. Even the poorest shepherds were his friends.

One night in December, Francis walked through the countryside visiting his friends, the shepherds. He stopped to pray to God for help in finding something special for the Midnight Mass on Christmas Eve. He had promised his friends in the village he would help them keep their Christmastide.

It was a cold, frosty night with the feeling of winter in the air. A full moon shone down upon the snow-capped mountains and hills around the village. Here and there Francis could see the glow of a shepherd's fading campfire. All around him sheep and goats were sleeping, crowded together in groups for warmth from the cold winter night. And near the campfire tired shepherds were sleeping soundly upon the frozen ground. It was a quiet night, but now and then the cry of a young lamb who had strayed from its mother could be heard.

Francis thought, "This night, with but few stars, and the shepherds sleeping on the ground, reminds me of the first Christmas at Bethlehem. I believe I now have an idea for my Christmas Eve services." And after visiting the shepherds, he walked homeward, planning every detail of his Christmas celebration.

But before he could complete his plans, he had to make a trip to Rome to see the Pope. When he saw the

Pope, he made known to him the plans he had for setting up a real Christmas crib at Greccio, Italy. He told the Pope his crib would help the people have a greater love for God. The Pope listened gladly, and gave his consent.

Leaving Rome, Francis arrived at Greccio just a few days before Christmas. He sent for his good friend, Vellita Giovanni, and told him of his plans.

Francis said, "I would like to represent the birth of the Christ Child just as it took place at Bethlehem. I want everyone who comes to see how the Infant Jesus was laid in a manger with the ox and the donkey standing by."

Vellita Giovanni, a good and holy man, said, "I will be glad to arrange all the details."

"Then we must hurry and prepare it," said Francis, "if we want to celebrate the Holy Nativity on Christmas Eve."

Vellita Giovanni quickly set to work and prepared the crib according to Francis' plans. Before the church he placed live animals in a manger filled with hay. In the stable he placed figures of the Blessed Virgin, Joseph, and the shepherds who came to adore the newborn Saviour. Men and women of the village happily prepared torches to light the night on which the Star of Bethlehem had risen.

Priests and people from every part of the country were asked to the midnight services at Greccio.

When the crib was ready, Francis looked about him and said, "I am well pleased. It is, indeed, another Bethlehem!"

The night of the Holy Nativity was as light as day. Men, women, and children came flocking to Greccio to see and hear Francis. The roads were filled with carts carrying people to the Christmas Eve services. The town was almost as crowded as Bethlehem was when Jesus was born.

Now when the people had gathered before the church, Francis showed them his Christmas crib, a real stable! There stood the manger full of hay, with ox and donkey, and the figures of the Blessed Virgin, Joseph, and the shepherds. The people looked on in wonder and delight at the first Christmas crib! They rejoiced, and the night overflowed with gladness.

Then, in the gentle voice they knew so well, Francis told them the story of the birth of the Christ Child in a manger at Bethlehem. He told them how the shepherds came to adore Him, and left Him gifts. He told them how the angels came down from heaven to sing the praises of the Holy Baby Jesus. He told how the Wise Men of the East, who followed the brightest of stars, came to the stable with gold, frankincense, and myrrh.

Francis said, "I want you to remember the greatest gift of all, God's everlasting gift of the Saviour."

The church bells rang out, and Francis helped to say

the Mass over the manger. He invited all those present to take part.

Later, when he knelt down to pray, there appeared in his arms a Child surrounded by a brilliant light!

Everyone fell upon his knees and gave praise to God. It was, indeed, a wonder night. Never had there been such a glorious celebration as there was that night in the tiny village of Greccio. And everyone returned home with joy and gladness in his heart.

And now every church and almost every home has a crib at Christmas time. People know that this beautiful custom represents the birthplace of the little Saviour at Bethlehem, and that the Christmas spirit of love is all around it.

☆
☆

MIRACLE OF THE BELLS

☆

☆

Many years ago, in northern Ireland, there was a beautiful little church that was the pride and joy of its people. It was very small, and had been built by their forefathers. For many years the peasant farmers had needed a church that was not so far away. The peasants were very poor, and it took a long time to raise enough money to finish the little country church.

But after forty years, the outside of the little church

and the altar were finished. For the next few years the farmers saved until they could furnish the church with pews, a stove, and an organ.

To people from outside the pleasant little valley, the church was very plain. But to the people who had built it, it was a beautiful thing. It was located in the center of the valley so that everyone had about the same distance to go to attend Mass and receive the Sacraments.

Now that the church was finished, the people needed a priest to say Mass and give the Sacraments. From a large parish in Belfast, a young priest was sent to be the first pastor.

It was nearing Christmas when all was ready for the celebration of the first Midnight Mass in the beautiful little church. It was the custom then that all those who came should bring an offering or gift to lay at the foot of the altar in honor of the Christ Child. And each offering was to be a good and useful gift, the nicest and most precious possession each owned. For these sturdy peasant farmers were happy that they now had a place to worship and were glad to make another sacrifice.

Miles away, three young children were making preparations to attend the Midnight Mass. Their names were Michael, Margarite, and Mary. Michael was ten and the oldest. Then came Margarite who was eight. Mary, the youngest, was six. Their parents could not go at midnight, so the children eagerly prepared for the eight-mile ride without them.

In their bedroom, Mary and Margarite talked about the gifts they were planning to give to the Christ Child. "Oh, Margarite," said Mary, "it will be so nice to see our own little church. Everyone says the altar is beautiful. What are you planning to give the Christ Child?"

And Margarite replied, "I am giving my pearl rosary. It is the most precious gift I have. You know, Mary, mother told us that nothing is too good for the Christ Child!"

Mary thought and thought about her gift to the Saviour. But nothing seemed quite nice enough. She knew she had only one thing that was precious, but she did not want to part with it. It was her sweet little doll lying in the wooden cradle. Her parents had given it to her just last Christmas. "Oh, but I can't part with the only doll I have!" she thought.

But after thinking about the little Jesus and all the things her mother told her about His coming to save the world, she quickly wrapped the doll to take to church.

It was bitterly cold that Christmas Eve. Snow was falling and covering the bare ground. Michael had hitched the horse to the sleigh and was waiting for Mary and Margarite. The children dressed in their warmest clothes and started off toward the church.

Halfway to the church, they discovered they were very cold. It was snowing harder now, and the cold wind seemed to go right through their clothes. Mary, the youngest, said, "Michael, could we stop at a farmhouse and warm ourselves? I am so cold."

"Yes, Mary, soon we will be at the Baker place," said Michael. "We will stop there. Perhaps Mrs. Baker will be kind enough to give us some lunch, too."

When they reached the Baker place, it was dark and deserted looking. But they stopped anyway, for Mary was crying that she was too cold to go on.

When the children knocked at the door, there was no answer. Michael tried the door and found it unlocked. They walked into the dark room. There was a lantern on the kitchen table. Michael found some matches and lit the lantern. "Hurry, Michael," said Mary, "and make a fire; my hands and feet are almost frozen."

Soon Michael had a nice fire going in the little stove at the end of the room. They warmed themselves, and as they were talking, they heard noises that seemed to come from the other room. They listened, but heard nothing. Margarite said, "It is only the wind howling."

A few minutes later, they heard the same sound. At first the children were frightened, but Michael said, "There is someone in the other room. I will take the lantern and see. You stay here."

"Come in, sisters," Michael called from the other room.

"Mrs. Baker and her little girl are here and sick in bed."

Margarite and Mary hurried into the bedroom. Margarite said, "Oh, Mrs. Baker, I am so sorry to find you this way. I will fix you both something to eat and drink." Then she told Mrs. Baker why they had stopped at her place. "We were so cold and needed to warm ourselves before going on to the Midnight Mass."

"It is all right, my child," Mrs. Baker said, glad that someone was here to help her.

The children left and went into the kitchen. Right away Margarite said, "I will stay with Mrs. Baker and her little girl. They are sick and need me. Here, Mary, take my rosary and offer it to the Christ Child for me. He will understand that I cannot be there."

Mary did not want to leave Margarite behind, because she knew how much her sister wanted to see the beautiful little church that her parents had talked so much about. She tried hard to keep the tears from falling down her cheeks. They had planned for so long to go together; now everything was changed.

But Mary got over her sadness because she was thinking about poor Mrs. Baker and her little girl lying so helpless in the next room. She was the lucky one; she could go to the Midnight Mass.

Mary felt sorry for the little Baker girl. She went over to the bed and laid her own precious little doll in the girl's arms. She had planned to give it to the Christ Child, but she felt that He would understand. And anyway, didn't the Bible say that what we do for others, we do for Christ Himself?

The little Baker girl smiled her thanks, and the tears in her eyes told Mary that she was very happy.

Mary walked away from the bed with a warm feeling inside. She knew she had brought happiness to another. She was glad that her mother had told her about Jesus, and how giving to others was the true meaning of Christmas.

Michael and Mary were warm now, and ready to go on to the church. They said good-by to Margarite and started off into the cold winter night.

Soon they were nearing the church. "Oh look, Michael," Mary said, "there are lighted candles in the windows. How pretty they are! Mother told me that the candle, glowing at Christmas, honors Jesus who is the Light of the World."

Inside the church, Mary and Michael looked about them and thought their church was beautiful.

After the Mass the people walked up one by one to the altar and placed a gift near the Christ Child in the manger. Mary was the last one, and she was so small no one really noticed her. She knelt down in front of the little Christ Child and laid her sister's rosary at His feet.

And just as everyone was about to leave, there came the sound of heavenly music, the sweetest melody ever

heard! Everyone sat breathlessly in the pews and wondered what it was.

Then they noticed a little girl kneeling before the crib.
It was Mary. Before her lay her sister's rosary. The bells
they heard were heavenly bells playing the most beautiful
music ever heard on earth. God was rewarding these good
people for remembering the true meaning of Christmas.
The Christ Child accepted Margarite's gift, though she
was not there to give it; and Mary's gift, though it was in
the arms of the little Baker girl far away.

"Inasmuch as you have done it unto one of the least
of My brethren, you have done it unto Me."

☆
☆

THE SAVIOUR'S CANDLE

☆
☆

Once, many years ago, a poor woman and her small son lived in a humble cottage at the edge of a village in Ireland.

The woman was a widow, and she was left alone to care for the young boy. To earn a living, she took in sewing and washing. Everyone liked her, because she was always good and kind. Whatever she had, she gladly shared with others.

During the Christmas season, she and her son always

lighted the Saviour's Candle, and placed it in the window of their home. It was the only house in the tiny village that had a candle burning in the window during the holy season. All night long the light shone, so that any weary traveler would see the light and come in for food and shelter. The door was kept unlocked, too, for it was a sign of friendliness and good will to leave the door ajar during the Christmas season.

The light from the widow's candle brought cheer and happiness to everyone in the village. They grew to depend on its being there to guide them homeward in case they were lost. And it did, many times.

One Christmas Eve, the flickering light helped a poor lost soldier find his way home. Another Christmas, a fierce blizzard came. The snow completely covered many of the small homes in the village. But the light of the Saviour's Candle, placed in the upstairs window, guided a group of school children that had been lost to her door. She gave them food, warmed their cold hands and feet, and put them to bed for the night. The next morning, after the snow had been shoveled from the village doors, the children returned safely to their homes.

Many Christmases came and went, but always a candle burned brightly in the window and sent a cheerful message to all who needed it.

There was a great potato famine one year, and by Christmas many of the people in the village had died from hunger, for the potato was the main food on the Irish family table. Many families lived on potatoes alone. Each family had a small tract of land and potatoes were the only food that grew well in the soil there.

In that same year, the Great War came. Many of the village sons went away to fight. It was a bad year all around: crops failed, there was much sickness, and many sons were killed in battle.

But through all the troubles that came to the village, the widow and her son were spared. Many said she led a charmed life. Others called her a living saint, for she often prayed and could be seen at Mass every morning of the year.

One day a certain man asked the widow, "Is it the beautiful candle in your window that keeps you from sickness and trouble?"

And the widow said, "The light of the candle shines forth as a message of love and hope, and to light the way of the Christ Child. Christmas is the birthday of the Saviour. He came into the world to save mankind, and to teach us the lesson of love: What we do for others, we do for Christ Himself."

The people of the village decided to place a Christmas candle in their windows too. So this Christmas Eve found every home with a lighted candle. The village looked bright and cheerful. The candles burned all night long. The next morning the little village church was filled with men, women, and children praying for the end of the war so their sons and brothers might come home.

And that very day, a messenger came with the good news that the war was over. Peace had come at last!

There was much rejoicing and happiness in the village that Christmas Day. Everyone said it was the candles burning in the windows that brought the Christ Child to their very doors. God had answered their prayers!

From that time on, it became a custom in Ireland to keep a candle burning in the window on Christmas Eve to light the way of the Christ Child.

And now, all over the world, the soft glow of the Christmas candles sends forth a message of love, hope, and cheer. The light of the candle reminds us that Christ is the Light of the World.

☆
☆

THE LITTLE STRANGER*

☆

☆

A LONG time ago, in the country of Germany, a poor
laborer and his wife lived in a small cottage at the edge
of the forest. The man was a woodcutter who made
but a scanty living for his family. They had two children,
Valentine and Mary. They were good children, and always did what they were told to do.

One cold winter evening, as the wind howled about the
small cottage, there came a faint knock at the door. And

* Adapted from "The Fir Tree," by Hans Christian Andersen.

then a child's voice was heard, crying, "I am cold and hungry. Please let me in!"

Mary and Valentine were a little frightened. But with brave hearts they went to the door and pulled it open. Standing before them was a little boy. His feet were bare, his clothes were thin and ragged, and he was shivering from the cold.

"Come in, you poor little child," the children said.

Mary and Valentine quickly made a place for him before the small blaze in the fireplace, depriving themselves of most of the warmth. And when the little stranger had warmed his cold hands and feet, they asked him if he would like something to eat.

"We have only some dry bread, but you may have it," said Mary. So the little stranger sat down and ate the dry bread.

Soon he grew warm and sleepy. The children said to him, "You must be tired, poor little child!" They asked him to sleep on their bed. This meant they would have to make themselves comfortable on hard wooden benches.

The little stranger said, "God will bless you for your kindness."

The children showed the little stranger to their bed. When he was asleep, they said to each other, "We should be thankful that we have a nice home and a warm bed to sleep in. The poor little stranger has nothing."

After their father and mother had gone to bed, Mary

and Valentine lay awake on the wooden benches near the fireplace. And before they fell asleep, they told each other how happy they were to have shared their home and bed with the little stranger.

But when they had finally fallen asleep, they were awakened by the sound of sweet music outside their cottage. Valentine and Mary sat up on their benches and listened to the music. Valentine said to Mary, "Do you hear the beautiful voices singing? What can it be?"

They hurried to the window. Standing before their home was a group of angel children dressed in shining robes and playing golden harps!

And as they watched, the little child they had sheltered came and stood before them. His ragged clothes and his hungry look were gone! He was dressed in shining robes and a golden light shone above his head!

In a soft voice he said, "I was cold and you took me in; I was hungry and you shared your food; I was tired and you let me sleep in your bed. I am the Christ Child, and I bring peace and happiness to good children everywhere."

Near the cottage grew a little fir tree. The Christ Child went out and broke a twig from this tree and planted it in the ground.

He said, "This twig shall become a tree, and shall grow fruit for you every year. This is to reward you for your kindness to me. I will bless you!"

Then he and the angel children disappeared. But the fir twig grew and became a beautiful tree, and on its branches hung fruit and nuts at Christmas time.

From this story we learn what Christ taught us, that what we do for others, we do for Christ Himself.

☆
☆

THE SONG FROM HEAVEN

☆

☆

JUST a few days before Christmas, in the year 1818, the organ in the church at Arnsdorf, near Salzburg, Austria, became unfit for use.

The parish priest, Father Joseph Mohr, was very much troubled. So he went to see his organist and friend Franz Gruber, and asked him what could be done.

"Soon it will be Christmas Eve, and I must have something special for the Midnight Mass," said Father Mohr.

"It is a bad time for the organ to be broken down. Do you think you could help me; for you know how everyone depends on music for the services?"

"Indeed, Father, I will help you," said Franz Gruber. "Do not worry. I will find something."

Now it happened, on a day before Christmas, the good Father Mohr was asked to visit at the cottage of a young woodcutter and his wife. For they were rejoicing over the birth of their first-born son, and were anxious that Father see the baby.

So Father walked through the cold winter night to the woodcutter's home. There he blessed the baby son.

It was late when he started for home. On the way, he thought about the lovely night and the newborn baby of which the parents were so proud. When he reached the top of a hill, he looked down over the peaceful valley below and saw the outline of the tiny village. Here and there a light could be seen in the darkness. The night was clear, cold, and quiet.

As he was standing there, he thought, "It must have been something like this that silent, holy night in Bethlehem when Jesus was born in the manger."

There were many things on his mind as he was walking homeward. He wanted to write a few lines of verse describing this beautiful night, and of the things he felt as he made his way to his home.

Upon reaching home, he wrote these words:

Silent night, holy night!
Bethlehem sleeps, yet what light
Floats around the holy pair,
Songs of angels fill the air
Strains of heavenly peace.

Silent night, holy night!
Shepherds first see the light,
Hear the Alleluias ring
Which the angel chorus sing,
Christ the Saviour is born!

Silent night, holy night!
Son of God! oh, what light
Radiates from Thy manger-bed
Over realms with darkness spread,
Thou in Bethlehem born.

The words pleased Father Mohr. The night was so much like the night when the little Saviour was born. And he had seen great joy on the woodcutter's face as he bent over his first-born son.

The next morning he took the verse to his friend Franz Gruber. "Franz," Father said, "I have written a few lines of verse. Would you help me put them to music? It will be something for the Midnight Mass on Christmas Eve."

So Father read the words, and Franz Gruber and his

wife listened. When Father had finished, Franz said, "The words are good. I will get my guitar and see what I can do for you."

Together they worked on the song. Soon they had caught the true spirit of the hymn. They both agreed it was just the thing for the Midnight Mass. And Franz Gruber said, "It is a song that should live forever in the hearts of all."

So at the Midnight Mass, the organ did not play as usual in the church at Arnsdorf. Instead, Father Mohr sang "Silent Night" while Franz Gruber played his guitar.

When the congregation heard the lovely words and the beautiful music, they were delighted. They all agreed that Father Mohr had, indeed, a special gift to give the Christ Child on His birthday.

Thereafter the song was sung by young and old alike, but was always a special part of the midnight services at the church.

The news of the beautiful song spread fast. An organ builder, who was repairing that organ that Christmas Eve, was so pleased with its melody he took it home with him. He engaged a well-known choral group of children, the famous Strasser sisters, to sing the song.

The sisters took the song with them to the annual fair where they sang it over and over for the people.

A famous composer, who was attending the fair, heard

the Strasser sisters singing "Silent Night." He was so pleased with its melody, he asked them if they would perform with his orchestra at a symphony honoring the King and Queen.

The girls were delighted, and made arrangements to go to Berlin.

There was much excitement that night in Berlin. When it was time for the girls to be presented, they proudly walked onto the stage. The lovely words and beautiful music seemed to cast a spell upon the people. A great calmness settled over the auditorium.

The Queen said to her husband, "I have never heard such a lovely song. We must find the composer and bring him to Berlin."

From Berlin, the song traveled to the great cities of Europe, and then to America. Today it is considered one of the most beautiful Christmas songs.